Dedicated to my wife, Kay

Fundamentals of
DIGITAL COMPUTERS

by MATTHEW MANDL

Lecturer in Electronic Technology
Technical Institute and Community College
Temple University

PRENTICE-HALL, INC.
Englewood Cliffs, N. J.

©—1958, by Prentice-Hall, Inc., Englewood Cliffs, N. J.

Library of Congress Catalog Card Number: 58–14304

First printing ....October, 1958
Second printing .....February, 1960

PRINTED IN THE UNITED STATES OF AMERICA
33308-C

Fundamentals of

DIGITAL COMPUTERS

PREFACE

Fundamentals of Digital Computers has been written to serve as an introduction to electronic principles as applied to modern digital computers. This book also covers the basic mathematical notation and codes used and explains how the various circuits and components are combined to form integral computer units. It is particularly suitable for those with no previous knowledge of computers, because the initial chapters review the fundamental aspects of signal waveforms and basic vacuum tube and transistor circuitry and also show their particular adaptation to basic computer circuitry. Technicians already at work in some specialized branch of the computer industry will find here substantial aid in acquiring a more rounded fundamental background with respect to the principles involved in all modern digital computers, whether general-purpose, special-purpose, or data-processing.

Particular attention has been devoted to the maintenance of a progressive topic sequence so that the over-all aspects of digital computers can be learned step-by-step. Subjects which might prove difficult, because of their complexity, have been given more detailed explanations, supplemented with tables and illustrations.

After the initial coverage of introductory material on *basic* computer circuitry, subsequent chapters discuss computer arithmetic and codes as well as the *special* circuitry and calculation processes formed by circuit combinations. Other chapters embrace the storage and programming factors and cover the methods employed for feeding information to the computer. The special features and basic aspects of a number of commercial computers are also considered, so that the reader can become acquainted with the essential differences in their general makeup. The final chapter is devoted to the service and maintenance problems associated with digital computers, which will be helpful to those who might be concerned with this type of work.

As an additional aid to study, review questions have been included at the end of each chapter. Also, because many special terms and phrases are employed in the digital computer field, a glossary has been provided for quick reference with respect to the definition of a particular word or phrase commonly used in the computer field.

The author appreciates the cooperation of the various computer companies who furnished detailed descriptions of their products. Grateful acknowledgment is also expressed for their permission to reproduce various photographs.

Matthew Mandl

Yardley, Pa.

CONTENTS

ix

CONTENTS

1
□ □
■ □ □
□ □ □
□ □ □

COMPUTERS
AND COMPONENTS

INTRODUCTION

Ever since man first learned to count and to use numbers for addition, multiplication, and other calculations, he has endeavored to simplify and speed up such processes by employing some means other than the tedious method of writing down the numbers and going through the rather slow mental procedures of calculating routines. Even before writing instruments were invented, at the dawn of civilization, the fingers of the hands were used for counting purposes. Use of the digits (digital counting) is undoubtedly the basis for our present day system of numbers using the base ten.

The earliest form of the digital type computer from which all modern computers—no matter how complex—stem, is the *abacus*. This simple, yet effective, digital machine finds mention in history as being used by the Egyptians as early as 450 B.C. In the form used then it consisted of a grooved clay board which used round pebbles in the grooves. Historical evidence indicates crude types of the abacus to have been employed even some centuries preceding its use by the Egyptians. Later, modified forms of the early abacus appeared in Japan, China, and other countries, and consisted of a

1

wood frame with wires or rods on which wood beads were strung. Each group of beads represents a "place" in the decimal system, such as tens, hundreds, thousands, etc. The abacus is still in use in China and Japan, and a skilled operator can compete in noteworthy fashion even with a modern desk type calculator with respect to speed in the common forms of addition, multiplication, etc.

In briefly summarizing the history of machine type computers, mention must be made of the Scottish mathematician John Napier (1550–1617) who made some valuable contributions to mathematics. Napier is credited with the invention of logarithms (1614) coining the word and publishing the famous tables. With John Briggs, he converted logarithms to the base 10 and also introduced the decimal point in numerical notations. Napier was also first to use tables of trigonometric functions. He originated a multiplication process which utilized numbering rods (1617). The numbering rods were often referred to as "Napier's Bones."

It wasn't until 1642, however, that the first type of adding machine or desk calculator appeared. This was invented by Blaise Pascal (1623–1662), the French scientist. The device employed simple wheels in the form of gears and its functions were confined solely to addition and subtraction. Subsequently, other mathematicians improved Pascal's earlier calculation device by the addition of the multiplication process employing repeated additions, but mechanical imperfections hampered progress.

It was the British mathematician Charles Babbage (1792–1871) who first conceived the idea of a calculator which would not only solve problems, but would also print out the answers. His idea was a mechanical calculator which could be fed a particular problem, would then proceed with the complete calculation without additional aid from the operator, and produce the answer in printed form. Early attempts to build the machine failed when the English government withdrew support and Babbage found it difficult to acquire precision components. In 1833, however, Babbage promoted an idea for a more complex computer which was in reality the forerunner of the modern digital computers. The machine was to be designed with programming (method and process of calculation) and memory (storage of numbers) sections, employing two sets of cards—the latter for purposes of selecting the type of operation to be performed and indicating the numerical values to be processed. The arithmetic processes were to be performed with toothed wheels. While Babbage's ideas were inspirational conceptions of an advanced nature, he encountered the drawbacks of imperfect materials and lack of finances; he did not have available the extraordinary simplicity accruing from electrical circuits.

The first key driven type of adding machine was patented as early as 1850, but it wasn't until 1886 that Dorr E. Felt brought out the first really practical key driven adding machine. This was patented in 1887 as the *Comptometer*, and in 1889 Felt added the printing feature (*Comptograph*) making it the first practical machine to print out answers. Subsequently, other desk type calculators appeared on the market, and by 1920 the development of small electric motors permitted the calculating machines to be electrified, simplifying ease of operation.

As industries grew in size, their record storage and computing requirements became more complex and intricate. The demand then arose for greater speed in the handling of accounts, filing of records, and maintaining bookkeeping processes. Coinciding with this demand for high speed was the rapid development of the electronics field, with the advent of diodes, vacuum tubes, and transistors, plus the design of appropriate circuits lending themselves to adaptation in computer circuitry. Hence, the design of all-electronic computers solved the problems of expanding business growth.

The first *special purpose* computer using the electrical principles (relays, etc.) was completed in 1940 by the Bell Telephone Laboratories. Special purpose computers in great variety have been manufactured since then. *Special purpose* types refer to machines designed to handle a particular task related to a particular business or project, such as the handling of airline passenger lists, traffic tabulations, keeping track of train schedules, etc.

The first *general purpose* digital computer also employing electrical principles on a large scale was developed by Harvard University in 1944 and built with the assistance of the International Business Machines Corporation. *General purpose* refers to the ability of a computer to handle a variety of mathematical problems.

The Harvard computer used electric relays and electromagnetic clutches in the arithmetic section, and punched cards were employed for feeding information into the machine as well as for storing mathematical data. Compared with all-electronic calculators, however, this computer had limited storage facilities and, because of its mechanical aspects, was incapable of the high speed operations performed by later types. Chronologically, however, it was the forerunner of modern digital computers.

Around 1942 the Moore School of Engineering of the University of Pennsylvania developed the first all-electronic type digital computer. This computer was named the ENIAC (Electronic Numerical Integrator and Calculator) and contained approximately 18,000 vacuum tubes. It was designed primarily for solving problems of trajectory for the Ballistics Research Laboratories at the Aberdeen Proving Grounds.

Subsequently, other electronic computers of large scale dimensions stemmed from the original ones developed, and included such types as the TRANSAC, BISMAC, MANIAC, SEAC, BINAC, UNIVAC, etc.

BASIC COMPUTER SECTIONS

The basic sections of a modern digital computer are shown in Fig. 1-1. They consist of input devices for entering the information

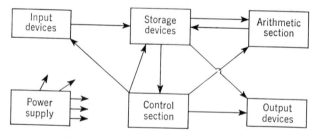

Fig. 1-1. Basic computer sections.

and calculation processes into the computer, storage devices for retaining information, control sections which operate the computer according to the instructions placed into the device, the arithmetic section where calculations are performed, and output devices which produce the results of the calculations and processes. In addition, a power supply unit furnishes the necessary voltage and current for the various circuits.

The sequence of instructions is placed into storage initially, in addition to the figures, numbers, and other data to be used in the calculations. The control section will then act on the instructions in storage by channeling the stored numbers to the respective parts of the arithmetic section. Once the calculation has been completed, the control section will either store the result of the calculations or will channel it to the output devices in accordance with the instructions which have been stored initially.

Figure 1-2 illustrates the various devices utilized in each section. The input devices can consist of punched cards, paper tape, or an

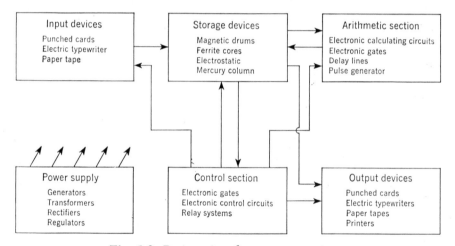

Fig. 1-2. Basic units of computer sections.

electric typewriter. These devices are used by the operator of the computer to place instructions and other information into the memory, as shown by the arrow from the input devices block to the storage devices block. The input consists of such information as instructions which are interpreted by the machine with respect to the processes involved in calculation, the various numbers or groups of numbers to be used in the arithmetic processes, as well as other alphabetic or numerical information.

The storage section of the computer may consist of magnetic

drums, ferrite cores, or other devices which have the ability to store electric signals. The storage section of the computer must obtain all the information and numbers related to a particular calculation or process from the input device before the computer can act on such information. Also, the storage devices may retain information to be used at a later date or store the results of calculations for reuse in subsequent arithmetic processes.

The control section of the computer contains electronic gating circuits, electronic control circuits, and in some computers mechanical relays which are tripped by electric pulses. The control section must interpret the information and instructions which are retained in the storage section, and it must transmit the results of such interpretations to the computer sections for initiating the calculation processes.

The arithmetic section contains adders, multipliers, dividers, and subtracters. These calculation devices are electronic and are made up of transistors, vacuum tubes, diodes, or a combination of these. Also in the arithmetic section are delay lines, amplifiers, and the generators which initiate the signals utilized. It is in the arithmetic section that calculations are performed at incredible speeds as compared to the ordinary desk calculators.

The results of the calculations or other processes performed by the computer are obtained from the output devices. The output devices can consist of punched cards which retain the information resulting from the calculations, or of paper tape which is also punched according to a specific code that interprets the results. Also employed are electric typewriters which automatically type out the information procured from the computer. Printers may be utilized which print one or more copies of the information obtained from the computer.

The power supply section consists of transformers, rectifiers, and voltage regulator devices quite similar to the power supplies for other electronic devices. The power supply itself may be fairly large when it must operate a computer having thousands of vacuum tubes. If transistors are employed primarily in the computer, the power supply requirements are not so severe and smaller units will be found.

The placement of information into the computer by means of the input devices is known as *read-in* and the procurement of information from the output devices is known as *read-out*. The instructions which indicate to the computer what processes are to be performed are coded, that is, specific alphabetic or numerical designations are given to each particular process. Locations of specific storage areas are also coded and each location is known as an *address*. An entire sequence of coded instructions, plus addresses, is known as a *program*. The application of all these terms, plus additional discussions of them, is covered in subsequent chapters.

COMPUTER FACTORS

Besides the *digital* type computer mentioned, there is also another type, the *analog* computer. Either of these electronic calculators is capable of solving problems with speeds far in excess of those obtained with the mechanical office type computers. Such electronic computers do complex calculations in a matter of minutes or hours which would, by older methods, normally take days, weeks, or even months.

The digital computer can be compared to the adding machine in its functional aspects, except that the electronic device will solve problems of a much more complex or involved nature than the desk type adding machine. It handles numbers, or coded alphabetic characters, and performs with them required calculations, comparisons, and other arithmetic functions. The digital computer is more versatile than the analog with respect to the nature and variety of work it can do, and in its design aspects, more simple.

The analog computer relates *physical* changes and variables (gear rotation, changes of shaft positions, etc.) in the form of mathematical equations. The analog computer, by analogy, thus interprets the physical changes and indicates the significance which such changes have with respect to the device or unit as a whole. The analog computer is useful in industrial automatic processes, guided missile and radar work, and other systems where the effects of physical variables must be mathematically coordinated for proper function and to achieve an end result. Analog computers are limited in application primarily to the problems related to a particular system. Such computers can be likened to the slide rule, and as with the latter, accuracy is limited by the design. For accuracy to a number of decimal places, an enormously large slide rule would have to be employed where fractional divisions can be ascertained. Actually, however, the accuracy and precision of computations in both types of computers are exceptionally good with respect to the type of problems each handles. A clarification of the essential differences requires a brief summary of the definitions of accuracy and precision with respect to computers. Accuracy in an electronic computer relates to how closely a solution of a problem approaches the actual answer. *Precision* of a solution is indicative of the closeness or sharpness of the answer to the actual sum. For instance, 3.14159 is of greater precision than 3.14, even though the latter suffices for a statement of the numerical value of *pi*. How precise a digital computer is relates to the capacity of the digits in any circuit group, and the degree of error in round-off. (Round-off errors are those which keep accumulating during the processing of a problem because of the rounding off of the various results or answers to the number of significant figures under consideration.)

In analog computers an increase in precision means design and circuitry increase, while in digital computers precision can be increased without any necessity of increasing the number of circuits, because an increase in precision can be obtained by increasing the time required for an answer. It is not unusual to encounter more than twenty significant figures in digital computers, while analog computers operate with four or five significant figures. The amount of precision required depends on application and can be built into the machine as required.

The comparison of digital and analog computers to the desk calculator and slide rule, respectively, is made only to indicate broad similarities. To carry the analogy further, the applications of the slide rule and the adding machine differ, even though there are a number of similar computations which can be handled by each device. So it is with the analog and digital computers; each has a specific application, even though in a broad sense there can be some overlapping of calculating operations.

PULSE SIGNALS

In a digital computer, the exceptional speed, accuracy, and precision are directly related to the type of signals and circuits which are used. To assure reliability, many of the computer circuits are designed to have stable states which are changed by use of pulse-type signals or voltage changes having a rather sharp rise time. Such pulses, either negative or positive, are employed for gating purposes, and for representation of the digit 1. The absence of a pulse may indicate 0, or hold a particular circuit in a certain desired state as more fully detailed in subsequent chapters.

In order to understand more clearly the application and usage of pulse signals in digital computers, it is necessary to make brief comparisons with other types of signals which may be found in other services. In *audio* amplifying systems, for instance, the type of signal with which the circuits are concerned consists primarily of alternating-current waveforms as shown in Fig. 1-3. At (A) is shown

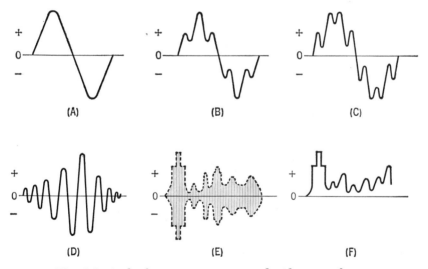

Fig. 1-3. Audio-frequency, carrier, and video waveforms.

a typical sinewave of alternating current. Such a sinewave consists of two parts: a positive polarity signal and negative polarity signal, as shown. This waveform could also be shown with the first part going in a negative direction and the second part going in a positive direction. Each section is called an alternation, and hence a typical a-c waveform consists of a positive alternation rising above the zero reference line and a negative alternation below the zero reference level. When each alternation of such an a-c waveform has the same duration as the other alternation, and each alternation has the same waveshape and amplitude as the other, a fundamental frequency is indicated. The type of a-c waveforms handled by audio systems, however, consists of complex waveforms because more than one frequency is handled. Also, musical instruments generate overtones or harmonics which consist of smaller amplitude tones having much higher frequencies but related to the fundamental frequency. Examples of such waveshapes of complex waveforms containing multiple frequencies are shown at (B) and (C) of Fig. 1-3.

For broadcasting purposes, all standard broadcasting systems utilize a-c waveforms at extremely high frequencies, known as radio frequencies (r-f), since the lower frequency radio waves cannot be transmitted properly. The carrier waveforms transmit or "carry" the audio or television waveforms containing the information which is to be sent. For amplitude modulation (used in standard radio transmission) the r-f waveform appears as shown at (D) of Fig. 1-3, and here the amplitude of the various alternations vary. The carrier waveform for television is shown at (E), and a much higher frequency is used than for AM broadcasting, but again the various alternations vary in their respective height.

In television, the *video* signals, which are procured from the detector in a receiver, also contain rectangular pulses as shown at (F) of Fig. 1-3. Such rectangular pulses act to trip the sweep oscillator in the receiver for synchronization of the beam trace of the picture across the face of the picture tube.

In computer systems, rectangular pulses will also be found, though such pulses are primarily of a constant amplitude and occur in no particular fixed sequence. Such pulses in their pure form are as represented at (A), (B), and (C) of Fig. 1-4. A rectangular pulse starts at a zero amplitude and has a sharp rise time to its maximum amplitude as shown at (A). This maximum amplitude is constant for a measurable duration, and then drops to zero again as shown. The edge of the rising portion of the pulse is known as the *leading edge,* and the decline of amplitude is known as the *trailing edge.* The duration of a pulse is an important factor in computer work as are also the rise time of the leading edge and the decline time of the

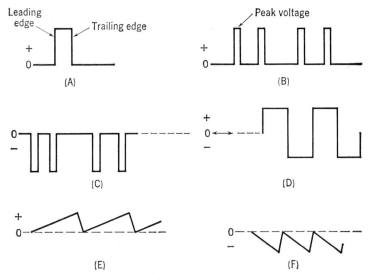

Fig. 1-4. Various waveforms.

trailing edge. As used in digital computers, the pulses may occur singly, in groups, or in a long sequence known as a *serial train.* Serial train refers to a group of pulses which arrive one at a time. Pulses can also be employed *in groups* with each pulse of the group applied to a separate transmission path to the circuits involved. Such a group, with pulses applied simultaneously, is referred to as being in *parallel form.* The time interval of the various pulses may vary considerably as shown at (B) and (C) of Fig. 1-4.

The polarity of the pulses may be either positive or negative, depending on the application in computers. A negative train of pulses is shown at (C), and they differ from those shown at (B) only in terms of polarity.

Another type of waveform which is also of concern in computer applications is the *square wave* illustrated at (D) of Fig. 1-4. A square wave superficially resembles a sinewave with respect to its having positive and negative waveform amplitudes which occur above and below a zero reference level. The square wave, however, instead of having a gradual incline and decline of alternations, has sharp rise and decline times similar to the leading and trailing edges of rectangular pulses. Thus, a *square wave* consists of a positive pulse and negative pulse which are joined, while a rectangular pulse is a solitary pulse which may be followed by others at fixed or random intervals.

While pulses are used extensively in the calculation circuits of digital computers, square waves are encountered in the generating circuits as more fully discussed later. The type of pulses shown at (E) and (F) of Fig. 1-4 are known as *sawtooth* waveforms and are used in oscilloscopes (see Chapter 9) or in other cathode ray devices where it is necessary to deflect an electron beam. The sawtooth waveform starts at zero and has a gradual rise time as shown at (E), then an abrupt decline to zero and again a gradual rise time. The waveform resembles the teeth of a saw and hence the term *sawtooth*. Both the positive-going and the negative-going sawtooth waveforms are employed for deflecting the beam in a cathode ray tube such as used in oscilloscopes and television receivers.

A pulse or a square wave is made up of a fundamental frequency plus a number of higher frequency components known as harmonics. For instance, a square wave has a fundamental frequency, a third harmonic of one-third the amplitude of the fundamental, a fifth harmonic of one-fifth the amplitude of the fundamental, a seventh harmonic of one-seventh the amplitude of the fundamental, and so on up to an order of approximately fifteen harmonics for a low frequency fundamental. For a higher frequency fundamental, the harmonic content may range up to 200, and for fundamental frequencies of approximately one microsecond for a complete cycle, harmonics may range well over a thousand.

Figure 1-5 is a basic illustration of how the fundamental and the harmonics make up a square wave. At (A), the sinewave marked No. 1 represents the fundamental frequency, and if this were 60 cycles the third harmonic would be 180 cycles. The third harmonic is represented by the sinewave form No. 2. Note that at the *point* of maximum amplitude of the fundamental, the latter is out of phase with the waveform of third harmonic at that point. Thus, the addition of these two waves at this point will result in a decline of the total (sum) amplitude. The harmonic frequencies, being higher than the fundamental, will not be in phase at some points and will be in phase at others. Thus, the harmonic components add and sub-

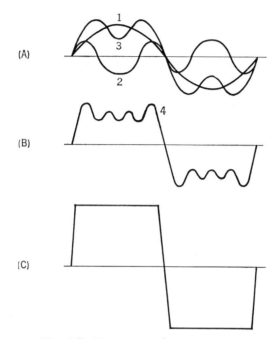

Fig. 1-5. Formation of square wave.

tract from the amplitude of the resultant wave. At (A), the resultant is designated as No. 3. When successive harmonic components are added to the fundamental, the original fundamental sinewave begins to have a steep leading and trailing edge, because at the beginning and end of each alternation ($\frac{1}{2}$ cycle) the phase of the harmonic components is such that amplitude increase occurs. Consequently, the addition of the fundamental plus the third, fifth, and seventh harmonics will produce a waveform such as shown at (B) of Fig. 1-5. Already the composite waveshape begins to resemble a square wave. When all the higher order odd harmonics are combined with the fundamental, the resultant will be a square wave such as shown at (C), which has a sharp rise time for the leading and trailing edges.

At (A) of Fig. 1-6 is shown a square wave with a frequency of

1,000,000 cycles (1 megacycle) per second. Each alternation occurs in 1/2,000,000 second ($\frac{1}{2}$ microsecond). At (B) is shown a pulse of $\frac{1}{2}$ microsecond duration, which occurs at the rate of 1,000 per second.

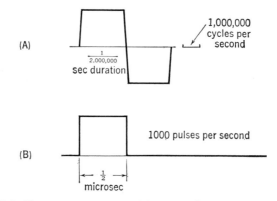

Fig. 1-6. Frequency vs. repetition rate in square waves and pulses.

Such isolated positive pulses are not connected to respective negative alternations, and thus can occur at 100, 200, 500, or any other such rate per second. The rate at which such pulses occur per second is known as the *repetition rate*. The repetition rate of a pulse can be regulated, regardless of the duration of the pulse. This is not the case with an unbroken chain of sinewaves or square waves, because for such waveforms the repetition rate of the individual alternations is fixed by the duration of the alternations.

Multiplying the duration of a pulse by the repetition rate provides a figure known as the *duty cycle*. Thus, if a 2 microsecond pulse is repeated 500 times per second, the duty cycle would be: $0.000002 \times 500 = 0.001$. The duty cycle also determines the average value of a pulse train. For sinewaves, the effective value is obtained by multiplying the peak value by 0.707, but this calculation cannot be applied to the pulse waveforms because of the bearing that the repetition rate has on the power that is developed. The average power can be considerably below the 0.707 value as shown in Fig. 1-7.

The average power may be ascertained by multiplying the duty cycle by the value of the peak power. Thus, if the duty cycle is

0.001 as in the foregoing example, and the peak power of the pulse is 30 watts, the average power would be:

$$0.001 \times 30 = 0.03 \text{ watt}$$

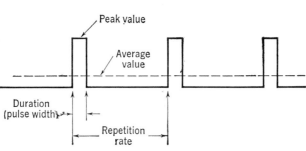

Fig. 1-7. Average value of pulse train.

Based on this formula, the duty cycle can be found by dividing the average power by the peak power:

$$\frac{\text{average}}{\text{peak}} = \text{duty cycle}, \qquad \frac{0.03}{30} = 0.001$$

As with the square wave, the pulse is composed of a number of harmonics, and the more narrow the pulse, the greater the harmonic content. The maximum number of harmonic frequencies which have sufficient amplitude to contribute significantly to the shape of the pulse varies inversely with respect to the pulse duration. Wide pulses may have significant harmonic components only up to the twentieth or thirtieth order, while narrow pulses may have harmonic frequencies to the hundredth or thousandth order, or more. The sharp rise of the leading edge of a pulse, as well as the sharp decline of the trailing edge, depends on the harmonic content of the pulse. If some of the higher frequency harmonics are lost as the pulse travels through circuitry, the pulse will be distorted, and the leading and trailing edges will assume a more pronounced slope with the result that circuit function may suffer with respect to accuracy in timing. Circuits handling a pulse should be able to pass all the significant frequencies contained in a pulse from the lowest to the highest.

A few of the lower frequency components of a pulse can be removed without materially impairing pulse shape, so that the lowest frequency to be passed is often based on the repetition rate of the pulse. For the higher order of harmonics, however, the amplifier or other circuit should be able to pass a frequency equivalent to:

$$\frac{1}{\text{duration}}$$

The result of this formula is sometimes referred to as the *base* frequency, and indicates that the amplifier should be capable of passing frequencies at least up to this figure if the essential formation of the pulse is to be retained. Thus, if a pulse has a duration of 1 microsecond, with a repetition rate of 1,000 per second, the base frequency is:

$$\frac{1}{1 \text{ microsecond}} = \frac{1}{0.000001} = 1 \text{ megacycle}$$

Hence, the circuit handling this pulse should be able to pass frequencies from the repetition rate (1,000 cycles) up to the base frequency (1,000,000 cycles).

If the pulse had a duration of 0.5 microsecond, with the same repetition rate as above (1,000), the base frequency would be:

$$\frac{1}{0.0000005} = 2,000,000 \text{ cycles} \ (2 \text{ megacycles})$$

Thus, the circuit should be able to pass frequencies within a range of 1,000 cycles to 2 megacycles.

The calculation for the base frequency does not take into consideration the repetition rate of the pulse, because the latter rate in no way affects the harmonic frequency content of the pulse. If, for instance, the 1 microsecond pulse had a repetition rate of 500 pulses per second (pps), the harmonic frequencies would simply occur more frequently, but the number contained in a pulse would remain the same.

PULSE DISTORTION

As mentioned, a circuit should be capable of passing all the significant frequencies contained in a pulse so as not to distort the waveshape of the pulse. In addition, the circuit should also have a flat response; that is, it should not pass some frequencies through it at lower amplitude than other frequencies. For a clearer understanding of the effect of circuit components on the waveshape of pulses, it is necessary to refer to the *time constant* curves shown in Fig. 1-8.

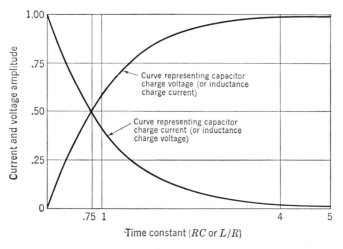

Fig. 1-8. Universal time constant curves.

The time constant is designed as *RC*, and indicates the resistance of the circuit is to be multiplied by the capacitance (resistance in ohms and capacity in farads). The chart in Fig. 1-8 shows the fraction of maximum voltage or current for any particular time constant. Thus, the two curves of the time constant chart indicate the amplitude changes of voltage and current in coils and capacitors. The curves rise in an exponential manner. You will note that the curve which begins at the lower left-hand corner at 0 represents the voltage rise in a capacitor when energy is applied through a resistor from a battery or other source. (This curve also represents the inductance current in a coil.) Thus, the lower left-hand curve indicates that when voltage is applied to a capacitor and resistor circuit, the voltage rises slowly as the capacitor is being charged. In an inductance, it shows the gradual current increase because of the back emf created in an inductance. The curve which starts at the upper left, indicating maximum amplitude, represents the capacitor charge current when voltage is first applied, or the inductance charge voltage. This indicates that in a capacitor current flow is maximum when energy is first applied to the circuit and gradually decreases as the voltage rises. In an inductance, the voltage is maximum initially but current builds up gradually.

The time constant of an RC circuit is the time required to charge the capacitor to approximately 63 per cent of its final voltage. It is found by multiplying the circuit resistance by the capacitance value. Thus, if a capacitor of 0.02 microfarad has a 5,000 ohm resistor in series with it, the time constant would be: $5,000 \times 0.02 = 100$ microseconds. Hence, at 100 microseconds the capacitor will be charged to 63 per cent of its full value. After five time constants the capacitor is considered as being fully charged with circuit current zero.

At (A) of Fig. 1-9 is shown a circuit which may be the coupling capacitor between two amplifier stages, with $R1$ acting as the grid leak for the input tube. If capacitor $C1$ has a sufficiently large value it will have a low reactance (opposition) for all frequencies and hence would reproduce a pulse applied to the input with good fidelity at the output. If capacitor $C1$, however, is of a small value, it will have a high reactance to the lower frequency components of a pulse. Thus, when a pulse is applied at the input, the leading edge indicates a sharp rise in voltage, and according to the exponential curve shown in Fig. 1-8, the maximum current would flow in the circuit as the capacitor charges. Thus, there would be an immediate high current flow through resistor $R1$, with the result that there would be a sharp rise in voltage across resistor $R1$. If the capacitor is small in value and charges fully as the steady-state flat top portion of the pulse arrives at the input, the current flow would decline to the capacitor and in consequence the voltage across the resistor would also decline as shown below the circuit drawing at (A) of Fig. 1-9. During the trailing edge of the pulse (indicating a decline in the voltage input) the charged capacitor would suddenly discharge through resistor $R1$, and current flow through the latter would be opposite to its direction during the charge of the capacitor. Thus, a negative voltage rise would occur. As soon as the capacitor discharged fully the voltage drop across $R1$ would fall to zero, as shown in the waveform drawing of (A).

When a pulse has been modified by a circuit such as shown at (A), the output is said to be a *differentiated* waveform. This means that the pulse has lost its low frequency components and the out-

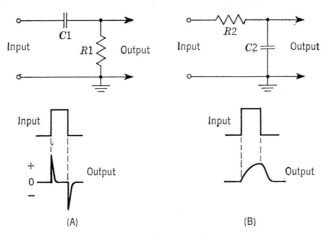

Fig. 1-9. Pulse modification.

put waveform consists primarily of the high frequency components. Thus, the original pulse shape has been changed because of the inadequate size of capacitor C1. On occasion, a differentiating circuit such as shown at (A) is employed deliberately in order to procure from the pulse the sharp leading edge for triggering purposes. The circuit is, in essence, a high-pass filter, since it permits the high frequency components of a pulse to go through the circuit but holds back the low frequency components. The circuit would have no effect in changing the waveshape of a sinewave, since the latter is not composed of harmonic frequencies. The only effect (other than a phase shift) that a differentiating circuit would have on a sinewave is to change its *amplitude* and not its *waveshape*.

When a circuit has an appreciable shunt capacitance such as might occur because of interelectrode capacitances in tubes, distributed capacitances in transformers, and the capacitance existing between the wires of a circuit and the chassis, the high frequency components of a pulse may encounter losses by being shunted to ground. This is illustrated at (B) of Fig. 1-9. Here, a circuit is shown in which a capacitor, C2, shunts the output terminals. Capacitor C2 can consist of any one of the previously mentioned capacitances, or combinations of them. When such capacities are sufficiently large, they will have a low reactance for the higher frequency signals of a pulse and hence will shunt the higher frequency signals to ground. Lower frequency signals, because they find a higher reactance in capacitor C2, will not be shunted so readily. Thus, a pulse applied to the input will appear as shown in the waveform drawing above (B) in Fig. 1-9. Note that the leading edge which indicates high frequency components now has a pronounced slant and the sharp corners of the waveform have also been lost. This waveform is known as an *integrated wave*, meaning the low frequency components of the pulse have been retained, but the high frequency components were diminished. The circuit, with shunt capacitance, is essentially a low-pass filter, permitting low frequency signals to get through, but diminishing highs. While such an integrating circuit is deliberately employed in television receivers, it is avoided in computer circuitry because pulses must retain all harmonic components. If a sufficient number of the odd harmonic components of the square wave are shunted, only the fundamental would remain, and the latter would then be a single frequency sinewave.

Thus, computer circuitry must be so designed that there is little effect on the waveshape of the pulses which are employed. On occasion, however, circuitry will affect the waveshape of the pulses even though precautions are taken to minimize such losses. When pulse distortion occurs, it may be necessary to take steps to reshape such pulses. This is more fully described in subsequent chapters.

Questions Relating to Chapter 1

    1. *a*) What was the first type of digital calculating machine?
      b) When did the first practical desk calculator appear?
      c) Who first conceived the idea of a calculator which would print out answers?
      d) When was the first general purpose digital computer developed?

    2. Briefly explain the differences between a special purpose and a general purpose computer.

3. Name the basic sections of a digital computer and give a description of their general purposes.

4. Briefly explain the basic differences between an analog computer and a digital computer.

5. *a*) Draw a sinewave, a square wave, and a pulse.
   b) Explain the essential differences, with respect to harmonic content and characteristics, of a sinewave, a square wave, and a pulse.

6. *a*) Define the terms "leading edge" and "trailing edge."
   b) Explain the differences between the repetition rate and duration of a pulse.
   c) What is meant by "duty cycle"?

7. What type of harmonics (odd or even) make up a square wave? What is the relative amplitude of the various harmonics which make up a square wave?

8. What factors contribute to pulse distortion? How is pulse distortion related to the time constant of a circuit?

9. Draw a differeniating and an integrating circuit and illustrate the type of waveforms which are produced for a pulse input.

10. What effect does a differentiating or an integrating circuit have on a sinewave signal input?

2

□ ■ □
□ □ □
□ □ □

Basic Circuits

INTRODUCTION

A complete digital computer is made up of a very large number of circuits, most of which are duplicates of a relatively small number of *basic* circuits. The circuits which are repetitive are those employed in the actual calculation processes, wherein several circuits are used many times in various combinations. Circuits that are not often repeated consist mainly of pulse generators employed for producing the signal waveforms necessary, a few limiting and clipping circuits for proper waveshaping and wave formation, and power supply circuits.

The circuits which are involved in addition, subtraction, and other computing functions are somewhat different from the ordinary circuitry found in radio and television receivers. Transistors and vacuum tubes, when functioning as amplifying circuits, have characteristics which change as the units age. Thus, the amplification characteristics of a tube may change slightly while in use, even though such a change is insufficient to hamper the normal amplifying properties of the circuit. For computer use, however, a slight change in characteristics might lead to erroneous results if the type of circuitry found in audio amplifiers is employed. Hence, in digital computers the majority of circuits use tubes and transistors in circuits which are operated under much more stable conditions, so that any change in the unit's characteristic will not impair so readily the accuracy and functional characteristics of the computer system. For this reason, crystal diodes, vacuum tubes, and transistors are operated in circuits which have *bistable* characteristics. This is done by designing a specific circuit so that the diodes, tubes, or transistors either *conduct* current or *do not* conduct current. This is far different from the manner in which a tube or transistor is operated in an amplifier handling audio or audio frequency signals. Under the latter application, the signal causes the tube to operate at *varying* current levels.

Some digital computers consist mostly of crystal diodes and a few vacuum tubes, some are composed primarily of vacuum tubes, and other computers utilize transistors to a greater degree than tubes or diodes. Crystal diodes, of the silicon or germanium type, are extensively employed since they have unidirectional current-carrying characteristics, providing a very high resistance for current flow in one direction and a relatively low resistance for current in the other direction. Vacuum tubes in diode, triode, and pentode form are also employed, though the modern trend in computer construction is toward the transistor. Use of the latter permits considerable saving in space, and because no power need be wasted in bringing a filament to high temperature, its power requirements are far below that for the vacuum tube. Some basic circuit applications for vacuum tubes are discussed in this chapter, and a summary of transistor functions is given at the end of the chapter.

CIRCUIT FUNDAMENTALS

The most commonly used bistable circuit in digital computers is the *Eccles-Jordan flip-flop* circuit. An understanding of this important circuit will be expedited if initially the fundamental characteristics of vacuum tubes are analyzed. For this reason, a review of the operational procedures of the simple circuit shown in Fig. 2-1 will serve as an introduction to the study of the basic flip-flop circuit as well as the generators, amplifiers, and other basic circuits encountered.

At (A) of Fig. 2-1 a simple vacuum tube circuit is shown, in which the plate (sometimes called anode) of a vacuum tube is at-

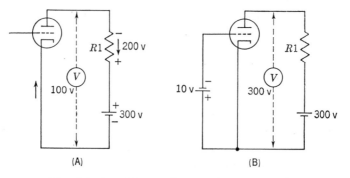

(A)   (B)

Fig. 2-1. Bistable conditions of vacuum tube.

tached to a resistor (R1) which in turn is connected to the positive terminal of a battery. The negative terminal of the battery is connected to the cathode of the vacuum tube. The direction of current flow through the vacuum tube is shown by the arrows, that is, from the minus terminal of the battery to the cathode, thence to the plate through resistor R1, and to the plus terminal of the battery. For the purposes of this discussion, the circuits shown in Fig. 2-1 have been stripped to their basic form for simplicity, and do not represent complete units.

The amount of current flow through a vacuum tube is limited by the battery potential, the circuit resistance, and the voltage applied to the grid. The grid shown for each tube in Fig. 2-1 is called a *control grid* because it acts as a gate and can regulate the amount of current flow within the tube. In the circuit shown at (A) of Fig. 2-1, however, there is no potential applied to the grid, and it has no effect on the current flow within the tube. Thus, in the absence of a negative grid voltage, a maximum current will flow through the tube, limited only by the emission capabilities of the cathode of the tube, and the resistance of R1 and that of the battery. For the purpose of this discussion, assume that this condition exists: maximum current is flowing through the tube (called saturation) and this current, flowing through resistor $R1$, causes a voltage drop of 200 volts across resistor $R1$. If a voltmeter were now placed from the plate of the vacuum tube to the cathode as shown by the dotted line at (A) of Fig. 2-1, the voltage which would be read would be 100 volts, since 200 volts of the 300 volt battery drop across the resistor $R1$.

If a battery is now placed between the grid of the tube and the cathode as shown at (B) of Fig. 2-1, the negative potential applied to the grid creates an electrostatic field around the grid wires within the vacuum tube. This negative-potential electrostatic field repels the negative electrons at the cathode (negative poles repel) and hence no current flow occurs within the tube. Since the tube current flow is now cut off, there is no current flow through resistor $R1$. In the absence of current flow through $R1$, there will be no voltage drop across this resistor. If a voltmeter is now placed from plate to cathode as shown by the dotted line at (B) of Fig. 2-1, a reading of 300 volts will be obtained.

As shown by the foregoing, (A) of Fig. 2-1 indicates one stable condition, i.e., saturation, while (B) of Fig. 2-1 shows another stable condition, that of cut-off. At (A), the plate-cathode voltage is 100, while at (B) the voltage across the plate and cathode is 300. The status of the circuit shown at (B) can be changed to that shown at (A) by simply removing the battery from the grid circuit.

Another manner in which the circuit shown at (B) can be changed from one state to another is by the application of a signal between grid and cathode. The voltage of the applied signal alters the applied grid battery voltage, as shown in Fig. 2-2. Here, the grid battery has been designated a C battery while the battery in the plate circuit of the tube has been designated a B battery. The battery furnishing filament voltage is usually known as an A battery. The latter has been omitted from the circuit shown in these figures to simplify the discussion, since it has no bearing on the operational characteristics of the tube. The A battery or A voltage serves only to heat the cathode to a temperature sufficient for liberating electrons for the purpose of conduction.

In Fig. 2-2, the C battery of 10 volts would normally be sufficient to cause the tube to reach cut-off (no current flow). If a short duration pulse type voltage is applied to the grid and cathode terminals as shown in Fig. 2-2, the positive polarity of the pulse will oppose the negative potential of the battery. If the pulse has

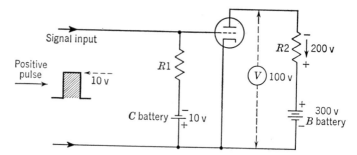

Fig. 2-2. A signal input voltage alters state.

an amplitude which is equal to or greater than the battery potential at the grid circuit, the C battery potential will be nullified and the status of the circuit will be similar to that of (A) in Fig. 2-1 where the tube operates at full current flow. Thus, the circuit shown in Fig. 2-2, will operate at saturation during the presence of a pulse at the grid input circuit, and will operate at cut-off during the absence of such a pulse.

The C battery can be dispensed with as shown in Fig. 2-3, by placing a resistor (R3) in the cathode circuit. This resistor will

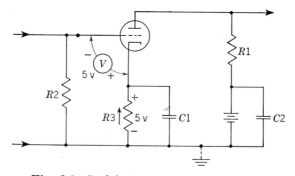

Fig. 2-3. Grid bias using cathode resistor.

furnish bias to the tube *during the time there is current flow in the circuit.* When the tube conducts, the current flow from the negative terminal of the battery to the cathode of the tube flows through resistor $R3$. This current flow causes the bottom of a resistor $R3$ to have a minus polarity and the top to have a plus polarity, as shown. This voltage drop across resistor $R3$ will make the grid minus with respect to the cathode by the amount of voltage drop across resistor $R3$. If this voltage drop is 5 volts as shown, the grid will be negative by 5 volts since it is connected to the bottom of resistor $R3$ by virtue of resistor $R2$. Thus, if a voltmeter is applied between the grid and cathode as shown, it would indicate that the grid has a minus potential of 5 volts.

The circuit, with bias developed by the cathode resistor, will not function as a circuit with two stable states because resistor $R3$ is unable to operate the tube at cut-off. If the voltage across $R3$ were sufficiently high to cut off the tube, there would be no current flow through the tube and hence no voltage drop across $R3$. With no voltage drop across $R3$, there would be no bias developed and hence the tube would conduct fully. This method of procuring bias by use of the cathode resistor, however, is extensively employed in amplifier circuits. In other circuits the means for overcoming the handicap of being unable to reach cut-off by the resistor $R3$ is handled in a special manner in the flip-flop circuit to be discussed later. Since, however, amplifying tubes are also used in computer systems, a brief review of the amplifying principle will prove of benefit here.

The circuit shown in Fig. 2-3 has been redrawn in Fig. 2-4 to

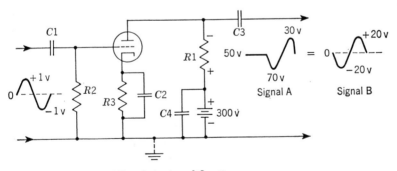

Fig. 2-4. Amplification process.

illustrate the operation of the tube as an amplifier. Assume that the voltage drop across resistor $R3$ is 5 volts and that the tube cut-off is at 10 volts. The operation of this tube can then be illustrated as shown in Fig. 2-5, which is a graph of the tube's characteristics. If a signal (such as an a-c waveform) is applied to the grid, it will

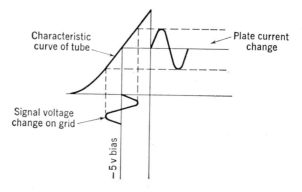

Fig. 2-5. Effect of grid voltage on plate current.

mean that a positive potential is applied to the grid for the duration of the first half of the input signal, and a negative potential for the duration of the second part. When the input signal is 1 volt, the positive portion of the signal will nullify 1 volt of the negative grid voltage developed by resistor R3, and current through the tube will increase.

For the negative part of the input signal, current through the tube will decrease, because the negative portion of the signal increases the negative potential at the grid. The resultant change in plate current causes a variation in the current flowing through R1, and in consequence there will be a change in the voltage drop across the latter resistor. As can be seen from Fig. 2-5, a positive portion of the incoming signal at the grid increases current flow through the tube and causes a greater voltage drop across R1. Because the voltage across R1 is in a negative direction, the voltage change may be from 50 volts to 70 volts. For a negative input signal at the grid, the decrease in current through the tube causes a decrease in voltage across R1 to 30 volts. This *changing* voltage across resistor R1 represents an amplified version of the signal applied to the grid. In the illustration shown, the change of voltage across R1 is 20 volts *positive* and 20 volts *negative*, as compared to the 1 volt positive and 1 volt negative signal applied to the grid. Hence, amplification has been procured.

Actually the voltage variations across resistor $R1$ are in the nature of a changing d-c signal, while the signal to the grid of the tube is an a-c signal. The output amplified signal can be converted to an a-c signal, however, by use of capacitor $C3$ which blocks the d-c level of the waveform, indicated as signal A, and converts it to the zero level waveform indicated as signal B in Fig. 2-4.

The voltage drop across resistor $R3$ which applies a negative voltage to the grid is known as *bias voltage*. Resistor $R2$ is known as the *grid leak*, because it permits a leakage from the grid of excessive electrons. Capacitors $C1$ and $C3$ are known as *coupling* capacitors since they couple signal energy from one circuit to another. Resistor $R1$ is usually known as the *load resistor* since it is across this resistor that the amplified signal energy develops.

Capacitor $C2$ helps to stabilize the voltage across $R3$ and, in effect, by-passes signal voltage variations which would occur at $R3$. Capacitor $C4$ places the bottom of $R1$ at signal ground, having the effect of shunting signals around the battery or power supply. Signal voltage variations across the internal resistance of the battery or other power source would constitute a loss of some signal energy.

Another type of amplifier often used is the grounded grid type shown in Fig. 2-6. In addition to its use in computers, the grounded

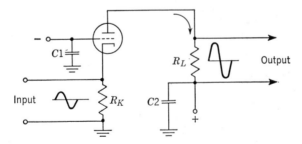

Fig. 2-6. Grounded grid amplifier.

grid has been extensively employed in r-f applications such as in the tuners of television receivers. The grounded grid amplifier permits the use of a triode at high frequencies without the need for neutralization. A triode, in resonant r-f stages, may oscillate and hence generate a signal which is undesired during the amplification process. Oscillations occur because of the capacity effects between the cathode and grid, and between the grid and anode of the tube. The coupling thus established causes regeneration and creates oscillations. In the grounded grid amplifier, however, the grid is at *signal ground,* and hence good isolation is provided between the input and output circuits with a minimum tendency toward oscillation.

In computer applications, the grounded grid amplifier is useful where a low input impedance and a high output impedance are desired without the phase reversal of the signal such as occurs across the amplifier discussed previously where the cathode is at signal ground.

As shown in Fig. 2-6, the grid of the triode is grounded for the signal via capacitor $C1$. A negative potential is applied to the grid for furnishing the operating bias. As a variation, the grid can be grounded directly, and bias procured by some other means, such as an additional cathode resistor.

Because the grid is at ground potential, the input signal is applied across the cathode resistor R_k. The variation of signal across the cathode resistor will cause a variation in plate current flow because it will affect the amount of grid bias. This bias change for signal input occurs even though the grid is grounded. Since the grid is at ground potential, a variation of voltage across the cathode resistor will increase or decrease the cathode voltage with respect to the grid. Increasing the positive cathode potential is the same as increasing negative grid voltage, and vice versa.

If the first alternation of the input signal is of positive polarity as shown in Fig. 2-6, it will increase the voltage across the cathode resistor and hence has the effect of increasing the negative grid voltage. In consequence, plate current declines with a consequent increase in the plate voltage signal as shown. Thus, the output signal across the load resistor R_L is in phase with the input signal as shown. The bottom of the load resistor is placed at ground potential in conventional fashion by capacitor $C2$.

The input impedance of the grounded grid amplifier is lower

than the standard grounded cathode type amplifier. Because of the lower input impedance, the grounded grid amplifier can be fed by the cathode follower type of circuit described later.

FLIP-FLOP CIRCUIT

A flip-flop circuit is a bistable electronic device extensively employed in computers. During operation, one of its stable states represents "1" and the other stable state represents "0." Signal pulses are used to trip the device and change it from one state to the other. When a signal pulse trips the flip-flop to register "1," the circuit is considered to be "set" and hence has stored a "1" numeral. If another pulse is applied to the circuit to reset or "clear" the circuit of the previously stored numeral, the circuit is considered to contain a 0 because it is in the cleared state.

When a signal pulse is applied to the input circuit, the flip-flop is "complemented." This term indicates that the circuit has been changed from one stable state to the other.

A basic version of the Eccles-Jordan flip-flop circuit is shown in Fig. 2-7. Here, two separate vacuum tubes are utilized, though a single envelope tube which contains both the triode (three element) tubes can be employed. Transistors can also be used instead of vacuum tubes.

In Fig. 2-7, the anode series resistors consist of $R1$ and $R2$. The signal energy developed across $R2$ in the form of a voltage change is coupled directly to the grid of $V2$ by the network consisting of the coupling resistor $R4$ shunted by the capacitor $C2$. For $V2$, the signal energy developed across $R1$ is coupled to the grid of $V1$ by the coupling network consisting of $R3$ and $C1$.

The grid of each tube is shown leaving the symbol circle at both right and left. Actually, however, the tube would have a single grid pin connection. The method of showing the grid extending out from both sides of the circle is extensively used for convenience in schematic drawing layout. Note that the grid of each tube has a negative potential applied to it via its own grid resistor. In practical circuits of this type, each grid resistor has the same value as the other, and each plate resistor also has a value equal to that of the other plate resistor. Thus, a balanced circuit is formed which is readily changed from one stable state to another. In order to make sure that the proper tube conducts initially, clearing pulses are ap-

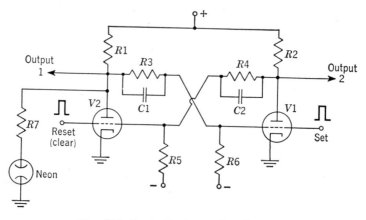

Fig. 2-7. Basic Eccles-Jordan flip-flop.

plied to the circuit as more fully detailed later. For the purpose of this discussion, however, assume that initially current rises through vacuum tube V2. The rising current through V2 establishes a voltage drop across R1, causing the voltage at the plate of V2 to decrease. The decreasing positive potential at the plate of V2 is also felt at the grid of V1, and hence the negative potential applied at the bottom of resistor R6 begins to predominate, causing a rising *negative* potential to appear at the grid of V1. This negative potential causes the current through V1 to decrease. The decreasing current through V1 lowers the voltage drop across resistor R2 and in consequence the voltage at the plate of V1 increases. This increase of potential at the plate of V1 also appears at the grid of V2 because of the directly coupled circuit. Consequently, the rising positive potential at the grid of V2 overcomes the negative potential applied via resistor R5, and this causes an additional increase of current through V2. The greater current through V2 creates a larger voltage drop across plate resistor R1.

The additional decrease of voltage at the plate of V2 again appears at the grid of V1 and the entire process continues until finally the negative potential at the grid of V1 is sufficient to cut off plate current flow through the latter tube. At such a time, the high positive potential at the plate of V1 which is coupled to the grid of V2 is sufficient to permit the latter tube to conduct a maximum amount of current for the conditions set up by the existing plate voltage and circuit components. Hence, V2 is operating at saturation, while V1 is at cut-off. The circuit will now remain in this stable state until a pulse is applied to change it to its second stable state.

The initial stable state is reached in a fraction of a second after power is applied. Because V2 is conducting heavily, the voltage drop across R1 is at a maximum level and therefore the voltage at the plate of V2 is at a minimum level. From the plate of V2 a resistor, R7, is connected in series with a neon light. Because of the low plate voltage at V2, however, there is an insufficient amount of potential present to cause the neon bulb to light. Hence, the circuit in this state is considered as representaitve of the digit 0 as indicated by the fact that the neon bulb *is not lit*. The circuit represents a "cleared" condition, where the word "clear" is synonymous with "zero."

If a positive pulse of proper amplitude is now applied to the grid of V1, it will overcome the negative potential existing at this grid and permit V1 to conduct. The current flow through V1 will cause a voltage drop across R2, and in consequence the anode voltage of V1 will decrease. This decreasing potential also appears at the grid of V2 and hence the negative voltage applied to the grid of V2 will predominate. In consequence, the current flow through V2 decreases, there is a decreasing voltage across R1, and then a rising plate voltage at V2. The increase in voltage at V2 also appears at the grid of V1, increasing plate current flow by an additional amount. The process continues until V1 is at saturation and V2 at cut-off. Anode voltage at V2 is now at a maximum and the circuit is now in its second stable state. The high voltage at the plate of V2 is now of sufficient amplitude to light the neon bulb indicator, and the circuit is now "set" and represents the numeral 1.

The neon bulb gives an indication because of the rise of plate potential at V2. This rise in plate potential also represents a positive-going signal and hence the plate circuit of V2 can be used as an output circuit as shown. Another output can be procured from the plate of V1. When this tube changes from cut-off to saturation, the plate voltage drops from its high value, this change representing a negative-going signal.

To clear the circuit so it will again represent the initial stable state (zero) a reset (clearing) pulse can be applied to the grid of V2. This positive pulse will overcome the negative potential at the grid of V2 which is holding the latter at cut-off, and will again permit current flow through this tube. In consequence the plate current rises and the voltage drop across R1 increases. Plate potential at V2 drops, and the neon bulb will go out. The lowered potential appears at the grid of V1 and permits the negative potential applied via R6 to predominate and cut off V1. When the circuit is cleared, a negative-going signal appears at output No. 1 and a positive-going signal appears at output No. 2.

Capacitors C1 and C2 shunt the direct coupling resistors R3 and R4 and help minimize the effects of interelectrode capacities. The capacitors are chosen to have a value larger than the interelectrode capacities of the tube to minimize the effects of the latter and to assure better "complementing": that is, changing the circuit from one stable state to the other. It is the characteristic of the shunting capacitor that voltage across it cannot change instantaneously, yet any change in voltage on one side of it is reflected directly as a change of voltage on the other side. When the flip-flop is complemented, there will be a very short interval of time during which *both* tubes are cut off. The grid capacitors permit proper voltage applications from the plate of one tube to the grid of another for assured triggering from one stable state to the other.

Because a flip-flop circuit of this type can be "triggered" from one stable state to another by the application of an input signal to the proper terminal, the circuit is sometimes referred to as a triggering circuit. More common, however, is the name *flip-flop* circuit.

In some computers, an additional neon indicator light is attached to the output No. 2 circuit of V1. When this is done, the neon indicator at output No. 2 will light up during the time the flip-flop is in the "off" state, while the neon bulb at output No. 1 will not be lit. When the circuit is triggered into its other stable state, the neon bulb at output No. 2 will go out, and the neon bulb at output No.

1 will go on. Thus, by the use of two neon lights, both the "on" and "off" conditions of each tube of the flip-flop circuit are shown at all times.

GENERATORS

The pulses which are employed for tripping the flip-flop type of circuit must be generated within the computer for use as desired. For such a generator, a vacuum tube or transistor oscillator is utilized. Oscillators generally fall into two categories: those generating sinewave types of signals and those producing square wave types of signals. The oscillators which generate sinewaves contain a circuit made up of capacitance and inductance for producing resonance. The resonant circuit formed by the capacitance and the inductance has the ability to interchange energy between the capacitor and inductor when a potential is applied across the resonant circuit. The applied potential charges the capacitor, and the latter in turn discharges across the inductor. After the capacitor has discharged across the inductor, the back emf of the inductor recharges the capacitor. This exchange of energy is known as *flywheel* effect and the process creates a sinewave signal.

Generators which produce square waves are made up of resistance-capacitance (*RC*) circuits which are not of a resonant character, but interchange signal information between two circuits of the oscillator. The most popular type of circuit utilized is an *RC* circuit known as the *relaxation oscillator* or *multivibrator*.

The most stable of the *sinewave* oscillators is the crystal oscillator illustrated in Fig. 2-8. The sinewaves which are produced can be employed for stabilizing the frequency of the relaxation oscillators, more fully described later, or the sinewaves themselves can be clipped and reamplified to form square waves.

As shown in Fig. 2-8 a crystal is employed in the grid circuit. The crystal is of the piezo quartz type and it generates an extremely stable frequency signal, the frequency depending on the type of crystal employed, its thickness, and the angle of cut with respect to the original crystal from which it was obtained. For extreme stability the crystal is placed in an enclosure and subjected to constant temperature.

When in operation, the crystal oscillator provides an ouput at the resonant circuit consisting of C1 and L1 in Fig. 2-8. The output signal is in the form of a train of sinewaves which are highly stable

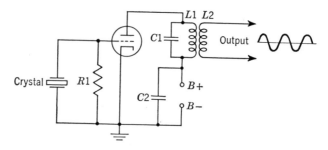

Fig. 2-8. Triode crystal oscillator.

in frequency. This signal energy may be coupled to a subsequent stage or circuit by the transformer arrangement made up of inductance L1 and inductance L2 as shown. Resistor R1 is the grid leak, and the capacitor C2 has a by-pass effect across the power source and returns the bottom of the plate resonant circuit to signal ground and cathode.

In the relaxation or multivibrator type of generator, two types are to be found. One is the plate coupled type shown at (A) of Fig. 2-9, and the other is the cathode coupled type shown at (B). Both these circuits somewhat resemble the flip-flop circuit discussed earlier, but the flip-flop circuit is not a generator since it will have no output unless it is pulsed. An oscillator or a generator, on the other hand, will generate a signal with a specific frequency whether or not a pulse is applied to its input. For the circuits shown in Fig. 2-9, synchronization inputs are provided so that the oscillator can be locked in for greater stability as more fully explained later. These oscillators, as well as the crystal oscillator previously discussed, are *free running*, which designation indicates that they generate a signal independent of a signal applied from an external source.

The circuit shown at (A) of Fig. 2-9 has somewhat similar characteristics to the flip-flop circuit previously discussed with respect to the fact that one tube conducts while the other is at cut-off. Assume, for instance, that the plate voltage of V1 is rising. This rise for plate voltage is coupled from V1 to the grid of V2 via coupling

capacitor C2. The change in grid potential in the positive direction
will increase current flow through V2. The increase in the current
flow through V2 will cause a greater voltage drop to occur across

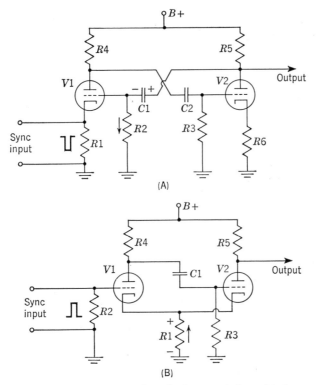

Fig. 2-9. Plate coupled and cathode coupled multivibrators.

resistor R5 and in consequence the voltage at the anode of V2 will
decrease. This decrease in anode voltage is coupled to the grid of
V1 by the capacitor C1. The decreasing voltage in the grid of V1
reduces current flow through V1 and raises the plate voltage of V1.
These conditions of rising and decreasing voltages for the various
tube elements can be seen in Fig. 2-10. The current flow through
V1 decreases until the tube is cut off, at which time a maximum
potential is developed at the plate. This voltage, coupled to the
grid of V2, causes the latter to have maximum current flow (saturation). Under such conditions a stable state has been reached since
one tube is cut off and the other is conducting fully. With the cir-

cuit shown at (A), only capacity coupling exists between the plate
of one tube and the grid of the other. Hence, the grid voltages cannot be held at a constant d-c level, since the coupling capacitors

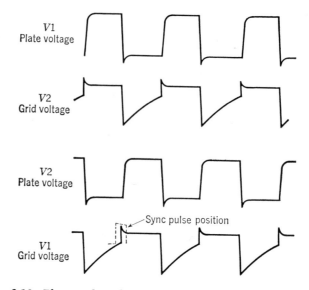

Fig. 2-10. Plate and grid voltage waveforms in multivibrator.

C1 and C2 are unable to hold a steady-state charge. The positive potential which was applied to the grid of V1 was sufficient to drive
the grid positive, and the latter drew current and charged capacitor
C1 with a polarity as indicated. As soon as a steady-state condition
exists, capacitor C1 will discharge through R2 as shown by the
arrow and in consequence the negative potential at the grid established by the charged capacitor will be reduced as the capacitor
charge leaks off thorugh R2. This can be seen from an inspection
of the waveform for the grid of V1. As shown in the bottom drawing
of Fig. 2-10, the negative voltage decreases gradually until finally
V1 can conduct again. When this tube conducts there will be an
increase in the voltage drop across R4, and the voltage at the plate
of V1 will decrease. This decreasing voltage is applied to the grid
of V2 via C2. Thus, the current flow through V2 decreases and the
voltage at the plate rises. This can be seen by a consideration of the
waveforms in Fig. 2-10. The rising plate voltage of V2 is coupled

to the grid of V1 via C1. The rising current through V1 increases
the voltage across R4 and hence decreases the voltage at V1. Eventually V1 is at saturation and V2 is at cut-off. At this point, C2 is
now charged with a negative potential at the grid. This capacitor
now discharges across R3 and the whole process is repeated.

As can be seen from Fig. 2-10, the plate voltage at V1 is in the
form of square waves which have a frequency depending on the resistance-capacitance components of the circuit. If the time constants of the coupling capacitors and grid leaks are altered, the
frequency will be affected. If, for instance, both the coupling capacitors and grid leaks were made larger, the capacitors would store
more energy and would take longer to discharge across the higher
value grid leaks. In consequence the rate of change with respect
to conduction and nonconduction of the tubes will be slowed down
and a lower frequency output signal will be produced. If the time
constant is made shorter by decreasing the capacitances, the resistances, or both, the tubes will change their conditions more rapidly
and a higher frequency is produced.

The application of a pulse across the cathode resistor R1 at (A)
of Fig. 2-9 will lock in the oscillator if the frequency of the synchronizing signal is not too different from the free running frequency
of the oscillator. If the synchronizing pulse arrives *at* or *near* the
time the grid reaches its conduction level, the circuit will be locked
in. The synchronizing pulse input at R1 must have a negative potential. This will make the cathode less positive with respect to the
grid, which is equivalent to lowering the negative grid potential
(the grid waveform rises *toward* the positive direction). This will
cause an increase in grid potential waveform as indicated by the
dotted outline in the lower waveform of Fig. 2-10. (A graph of
decreasing the negative grid signal from a high minus value to some
lower value, would appear as a rise, because the grid potential is
coming *up* from its former negative point.)

The oscillator shown at (A) of Fig. 2-9 would tend also to be
locked in by a sinewave type of signal, if the alternation of the sinewave which provides the lock-in is in a negative direction at or
near the time when the grid is reaching conduction.

The circuit shown at (B) functions similarly to the one shown at (A) and the same waveforms are produced as shown in Fig. 2-10. The difference, however, is that the energy exchange between the two tubes is accomplished by the common cathode resistor R1. First, assume that V1 has a rising plate voltage and that this is coupled to the grid of V2 via C1. Tube V2 will conduct heavily and the voltage at the plate will decrease in a negative direction. The increasing current through V2 establishes a large voltage drop across R1 with a polarity such as shown. Since the cathode is becoming more positive, the grid of V1 is, in effect, becoming more negative. Current flow through R4 therefore decreases and hence the voltage at the plate of V1 rises. This rising voltage is coupled via C1 to the grid of V2 until the latter tube reaches saturation and full conduction. When V2 has reached saturation, V1 will be beyond cut-off.

After V1 has reached cut-off, the steady-state positive potential at V1 will no longer appear at the grid of V2 since capacitor C1 is unable to couple the d-c voltage. Hence, the positive voltage at the grid of V2 declines. Current flow through V2 will start to decrease and in consequence the voltage across R1 also decreases. Thus, the relatively negative grid voltage will also decline until V1 can again conduct. When this occurs, there will be an increase in the voltage across R4 and a decrease in the plate potential of V1. This decreasing potential is applied to the grid of V2 via C1 causing an additional current decrease through V2. This lowers the voltage across R1 to a greater degree making the grid less negative at V1. The voltage drop across R4 increases additionally and the plate voltage at V1 declines to a lower level. The latter decline appears at the grid of V2 and drives V2 to cut-off, with V1 at full current flow. Again, the steady-state negative voltage at V1 plate is not sustained at the grid of V2 because of the capacitor action of C1 and the entire cycle repeats itself. (During the time when the grid of V2 is driven in the positive region, capacitor C1 charges with a negative polarity at the grid of V2 and a positive polarity at the grid of V1. Capacitor C1 then discharges across R3 to start the cycle all over again.)

As in the circuit shown at (A), a synchronizing pulse can be applied to the grid of V1 to stabilize the frequency of the cathode coupled multivibrator. The polarity of the sync pulse applied to the grid must be positive.

In computer terminology, the series of pulses which are procured from a generator system at a uniform repetition rate are often referred to as *clock pulses* because they are essentially "clocked" or controlled to provide such a timed pulse train. The usual pulse source in a computer is a free running multivibrator; that is, the multivibrator is of the type which produces output signals continuously such as the two just discussed. The pulses so obtained applied to a ring counter circuit of the type more fully described later. The signals from the circuits of the two counter stages consist of the control and gating pulses required in the various sections of the computer for its operation.

The previous *RC* relaxation oscillators generate a continuous pulse form type of output, whether or not a synchronizing pulse is applied to the input. Another type of *RC* multivibrator is the so-called single shot or "start-stop" type. This differs from the plate coupled multivibrator and the cathode coupled multivibrator because it does not generate a continuous output. Instead, it resembles somewhat the flip-flop circuit discussed previously. In the flip-flop circuit, however, the output alternates between a positive waveform and a negative waveform. In the single shot multivibrator, on the other hand, the output pulse which is developed by the application of an input pulse will always have the same polarity. Whether the polarity is a positive or a negative pulse depends on the manner in which the output terminal is connected to the circuit. The basic diagram for the single shot multivibrator is shown in Fig. 2-11.

This circuit is almost identical with the plate coupled multivibrator, except that a negative potential is applied to the grid of V1 through resistor $R1$. This negative potential is sufficient to hold V1 beyond the cut-off region. If, for instance, cut-off is minus 20 volts, the applied negative potential to the grid of V1 would be approximately 50 volts. Tube V2, however, has no negative potential applied to its grid and hence it conducts continuously. While conducting, the current through $R4$ would create a voltage drop across the latter and the plate voltage would equal the power supply voltage minus the drop across $R4$. For example, the plate supply voltage could be 300 volts, with 200 volts dropping across R4, leaving a volt-age at the anode of V2 of 100 volts.

The input pulse is applied to the grid of V1, and the pulse must have a positive amplitude sufficiently high to overcome the negative

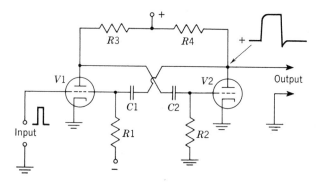

Fig. 2-11. Single-shot multivibrator.

voltage applied to the grid. If cut-off is minus 20 volts, and the negative voltage at the grid is minus 50 volts, the required amplitude of the positive pulse must be greater than 30 volts. When such a pulse appears at the input, V1 conducts and the voltage drop across the load resistor for V1 (R3) increases. Hence, the voltage at V1 decreases and this change from a high potential to a low potential is felt at the grid of V2. The decreasing signal at the grid of V2 de-creases current flow through this tube and less voltage drop occurs across R4, so that the plate voltage at the anode of V2 increases. The increase of plate potential is coupled to the grid of V1 via capacitor C1 and causes an additional increase in current flow through the latter tube. A greater voltage drop occurs across R3 and the increased voltage change is felt at the grid of V2. The re-amplification process eventually drives tube V2 into cut-off, and in consequence there is no voltage drop across R4. Hence, the full power supply voltage appears at the plate of V2.

If the plate voltage of V2 originally was 100 volts, there would be a rise to 300 volts upon the application of the input pulse to the grid of V1. The high potential at V2 remains at its maximum level for a short period. Capacitor C1, having been charged to some positive value must discharge to the point where the negative po-tential at the grid is at the point where V1 is cut off. Tube V2 starts to conduct again and the high plate voltage decreases and levels off at the normal value. Thus, a positive polarity output pulse of a predetermined duration is secured for every input pulse. The duration of the input pulses can be short, and will have no appreciable effect on the duration of the output pulses, since the duration of the output pulses is determined by the RC constants. For the circuit shown in Fig. 2-11, a phase inverter tube can be employed if the output pulse from the system is to be negative.

The circuit diagram of the single shot multivibrator shown in Fig. 2-11 is a basic type, and additional components or circuit variations will be encountered. One variation is to return resistor $R1$ to ground and apply a positive voltage to the cathode of $V1$. A positive voltage at the cathode of $V1$ will make the grid negative with respect to the positive cathode. If a positive voltage of sufficient amplitude is applied to the cathode of $V1$, the latter tube can be driven to cut-off. Another variation consists of the application of the input pulse to the cathode of $V1$. When the input pulse is applied to the cathode, however, the pulse must have a negative polarity because making the cathode negative will cause the negative grid voltage to decrease (in a positive direction).

A negative pulse can also be used to trigger the circuit shown in Fig. 2-11 by applying such a negative pulse to the plate of $V1$ or to the grid of $V2$. A negative pulse at either of these two points will decrease the current flow through $V2$ (and $R4$). This current decrease causes a rise in the plate potential at $V2$ and the rising signal potential is coupled to the grid of $V1$ via $C1$. Tube $V1$ will go into conduction and the decreasing potential at the anode of $V1$ will be coupled to the grid of $V2$ via capacitor $C2$, and again a positive pulse is developed at the anode of $V2$.

CLIPPERS, LIMITERS, AND CLAMPERS

Clipping circuits have various applications in computers, among the most important being the following:

1) Clip and hold pulses at a constant level.
2) Clip noise or other undesired signals from the peaks of the pulse signals.
3) Clip sinewaves to form square waves.

Clipping circuits can be designed to remove portions of the signal above a prescribed clipping level, or to remove portions of the signal below a prescribed clipping level. The two basic types of clipping circuits are the shunt clippers and the series clippers. Both are illustrated in Fig. 2-12.

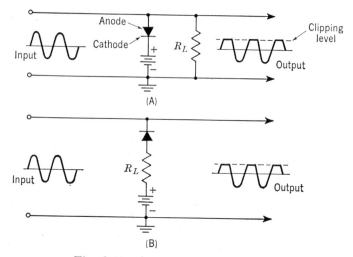

Fig. 2-12. Shunt and series clipping.

The clippers shown are the crystal diode types, though vacuum tube diodes could also be used. Crystal diodes can be of the germanium or silicon types, and their characteristics are somewhat different from the vacuum tube diode. A vacuum tube diode can be conducting or nonconducting, but the crystal diode does not achieve a nonconducting state comparable to the vacuum tube. The crystal diode has a reverse or back current flow, because with the application of one polarity a diode may still have some resistance even though such resistance is appreciably higher than when the diode polarities are reversed. Some diodes may have a forward impedance of approximately 200 ohms and a reverse impedance of 1 or 2 megohms. Crystal diodes sometimes have the cathode section marked with a plus sign which indicates the direction toward which the current flows during its forward current state.

The circuit shown at (A) of Fig. 2-12 is known as a shunt clipper because the clipping diode (and bias battery) shunt the load resistor R_L. This type of circuit clips off that portion of the signal which is above the bias level voltage established by the battery or other bias source. During the positive alternation of the input signal the diode conducts and the resulting low resistance shunts the load resistance and loads down the latter. As soon as the positive alternation of the input signal has reached the diode conduction level, no additional change occurs across the load resistor and hence the output signal assumes a flat top as shown. When the first alternation of the input signal declines to the point where the diode cuts off, the input signal then appears across the load resistor without being clipped. When a bias voltage is used, it causes the input signal to be clipped at the level where the input signal voltage exceeds the bias voltage. Hence, the amplitude of the bias voltage sets the clipping level and determines which portions of the input signal are reproduced at the output. If the bias voltage is omitted, all of the positive portion of the input signal would be clipped, and the output would consist of only the negative sections of the input signal.

At (B) of Fig. 2-12 is shown the series clipper circuit. This is designated as a series clipper because the crystal diode is in series with the load resistor (and bias voltage source). If the input signal consists of a positive alternation, an output voltage will appear as the input signal voltage is rising. As soon as the input signal potential reaches a level which is greater than the positive bias voltage, the cathode of the crystal diode will then be more positive than the anode, and the diode, in its reverse current state, has a high resistance which levels off the voltage at the output. This leveling occurs because all of the signal voltage appears across the high resistance diode. When the positive alternation of the input signal declines below the bias voltage, the diode resistance is decreased and the signal will then appear again at the output as shown.

As with the shunt limiter, the bias voltage can be eliminated when it is desired that all of the positive half of the signal is to be removed.

Both the shunt and the series clippers can be designed to clip the negative portion of the signal instead of the positive by reversing the crystal connections and the bias polarity.

A crystal diode can also be used as a clamper which will hold either the positive or the negative portions of a signal to a prescribed level. A clamper circuit is employed to maintain the d-c reference level of pulse waveforms. Such a d-c reference level is lost when the signal is coupled through a transformer or capacitor, or is amplified by a vacuum tube. The resultant is a waveform which has positive and negative alternations above and below a reference level (a-c). A clamping circuit restores the d-c reference level and maintains the latter with respect to the signal amplitude.

Typical clamping circuits are shown in Fig. 2-13. At (A) the

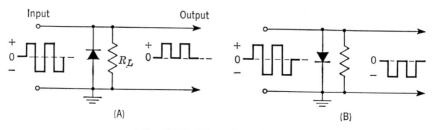

Fig. 2-13. Clamping circuits.

output signal is positive, since it extends above the established reference level. At (B) the output signal is negative, being below the established reference level.

As with the clippers previously discussed, the clamper uses crystal diodes, though vacuum tube diodes could also be employed. For the circuit shown at (A) the diode will conduct only during the negative portions of the input signal, and hence will present a low shunting resistance across the load resistor. When the input signal has a plus polarity, however, the crystal is in its reverse state and offers a very high impedance with negligible shunting effect across the load resistor. Hence, the positive portion of the input signal is reproduced at the output.

For the circuit shown at (B) the diode will conduct for the positive portions of the signal, and hence will act as a low shunt resistance across the load resistor. For the negative portions of the signal, however, the reverse resistance of the diode is high and the negative portion of the input waveform is produced at the output.

A vacuum tube can also be used for limiting (as well as for clipping) purposes, as shown in Fig. 2-14. A triode or a pentode tube can be employed, as desired. For the circuit shown at (A) a negative d-c potential is applied to the grid, of sufficient amplitude so

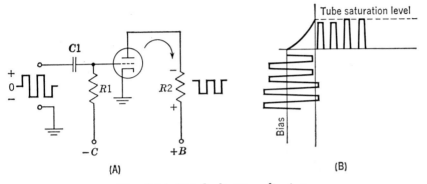

Fig. 2-14. Triode limiting-clipping.

that the tube is cut off. Thus, negative excursions of the input square wave will travel farther into the cut-off region and in consequence only the positive waveforms will cause tube conduction. The single polarity pulses developed across the load resistor R2 are of a negative polarity as shown, since there is a phase reversal of a signal *voltage* across a vacuum tube. If the amplitude of the incoming square wave is sufficient to drive the grid into the positive region as shown for the third and fourth positive alternations of the input signal at (B) of Fig. 2-14, clipping will be accomplished.

If the circuit is to function continuously as a clipper as well as a limiter, the positive-going grid can be utilized to develop its own cut-off bias by charging up the grid capacitor C1 and permitting it to discharge across grid leak R1.

The circuit shown at (A) of Fig. 2-14 can also be employed for sinewave limiting and clipping as shown at (A) of Fig. 2-15. The limiting of the output to only the positive alternations of the input sinewave, plus the clipping of the peaks, result in the formation of pulses which have a rather sloping edge. These pulses can, however, be amplified an additional amount and clipped by added clipper circuits until a fairly sharp rise time and decline time are procured in the leading and trailing edges.

A clipper can, of course, also be utilized solely to clip peaks without limiting the output with respect to a square wave input. For instance, the input can be employed as shown in (B) of Fig. 2-15, where the input consists of pulses, and the output consists of

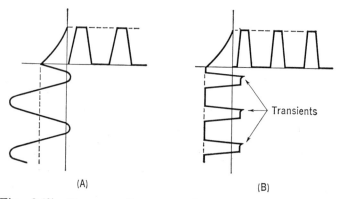

(A)

(B)

Fig. 2-15. Sinewave limiting and pulse amplification and clipping.

the identical pulses except for the fact that they have been clipped to eliminate the transients appearing on the peaks.

A typical application of a clipper circuit is shown in Fig. 2-16. Here, a start-stop multivibrator is preceded by a clipper tube V1.

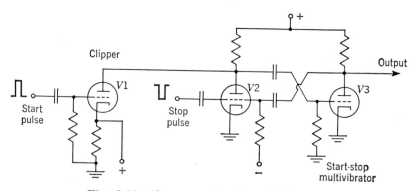

Fig. 2-16. Clipper used with multivibrator.

This tube is biased beyond cut-off by the application of a positive voltage to the cathode which causes the grid to be sufficiently nega- tive to cut off plate current flow in V1. A positive pulse is applied to the grid input of V1, such a pulse having sufficient amplitude to cause the plate current flow in V1 to reach a maximum. The rise in plate current of V1 produces a signal at the plate of V2 (and at the grid of V3) which has a negative polarity, and hence will trip the start-stop multivibrator and produce an output pulse. As explained earlier for this multivibrator circuit, the pulse duration developed at the output will depend on the time constants of the grid capacitors and resistors.

The starting pulse is of short duration, and during its absence V1 presents an open circuit at the plate of V2. Clipper tube V1 not only clips the peaks of the input signal, but also sharpens the triggering pulse and amplifies the starting pulse for application to the multivibrator.

The output pulse from the start-stop multivibrator can be used as a gating pulse for other circuits. A gating pulse, as more fully explained later, can be utilized to "open" or "close" a circuit. If the gating pulse is to have a prescribed duration, the RC constants can be adjusted to do this, or a stop pulse can be inserted at the grid of V2 to stop the multivibrator at some time before the circuit constants would normally cause the multivibrator to revert to its former state.

For production of the sawtooth waveforms discussed in Chapter 1, a discharge tube is employed such as shown in Fig. 2-17. Here,

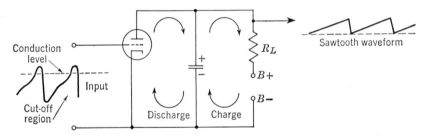

Fig. 2-17. Discharge tube.

a capacitor is placed between plate and ground (cathode) of the discharge circuit and this capacitor also shunts the output load resistor (R_L) as well as the power supply voltage. The input of this discharge circuit is attached to the grid circuit of the multivibrator generator or to some other such signal source. During the time that the grid of the multivibrator is at cut-off, the cut-off (negative) grid voltage also appears on the grid of the discharge tube and prevents it from conducting. During this time, however, the power supply of the discharge circuit will charge up the capacitor with a polarity as shown. Because of the load resistor and the slow rise time of the voltage across a charging capacitor (see Fig. 1-8), the voltage builds up gradually across the capacitor from a zero charge level. When the grid is driven into the positive region by virtue of the multivibrator grid's signal reaching the conduction level, the discharge tube conducts suddenly and in consequence has a low internal resistance. Since this tube shunts the capacitor, the sudden appearance of a low resistance path permits the capacitor to discharge through the tube. Consequently, the voltage drop across the capacitor falls to zero and a sawtooth of voltage appears at the output. When the grid signal goes into cut-off region again, the tube stops conducting and hence presents a very high resistance for the capacitor. Thus, the capacitor is enabled to charge again in gradual fashion to produce a rising output level. When the grid is driven into the positive region, conduction again occurs and the capacitor discharges. Thus, for every pulse generated in the multivibrator, a coinciding sawtooth voltage is produced at the output of the discharge tube.

For the formation of a pure sawtooth, the grid signal must have sufficient width to permit full discharge of the capacitor. The sawtooth waveform thus developed finds application in cathode ray beam deflection as mentioned in Chapter 1.

CATHODE FOLLOWER CIRCUITS

A cathode follower circuit is utilized for stepping down a high impedance to a low impedance in a fashion similar to the impedance step-down procured from a transformer. With a transformer, however, pulse distortion may occur, because the distributed capacitances of the transformer such as exist between the individual turns and the layers of the coil winding will shunt some of the high frequency components of a pulse. A transformer also has an uneven response to various frequencies because the reactance of a transformer changes with frequency.

The cathode follower type of circuit such as shown at (A) of Fig. 2-18 has a wide frequency response and is capable of transferring a pulse from a high impedance circuit to a low impedance circuit or a low impedance network such as a coaxial cable.

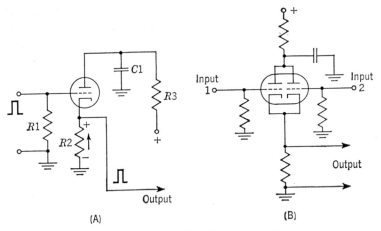

Fig. 2-18. Cathode follower circuits.

As shown at (A), the output from the circuit is derived from across the cathode resistor R2. There is no signal developed in the plate circuit because capacitor C1 will by-pass signal components to ground. Hence, the resistor R3 in series with the B voltage is *not* a load resistor but only functions as a voltage dropping unit.

When a positive pulse signal is applied across the input as shown, there will be an increase in plate current flow through the vacuum tube and hence an increase in the current through the cathode resistor R2. This increase in plate current will result in a voltage rise across the cathode resistor and such a voltage rise will "follow" the grid signal. The fact that the cathode signal which is produced follows the grid signal in terms of polarity and waveshape is the reason for the circuit being known as a cathode follower.

The cathode follower circuit is not a voltage amplifier, since the output signal voltage is lower in amplitude than the input signal. Signal voltage gain is less than unity but the loss of signal amplitude across the cathode follower is unimportant since the amplitude can be made more than adequate before application to the cathode follower, or the signal at the output of the cathode follower can be amplified to the required amount in subsequent stages.

Current flow through resistor R2 will establish a grid bias voltage, but the absence of the usual cathode capacitor by-pass causes degeneration. The by-pass capacitor must be omitted to permit signal voltage variations to occur across resistor R2. The signal voltage which develops across R2, however, acts inversely to the bias which would be developed and hence decreases the signal amplitude. For instance, a plus pulse at the grid has the effect of *decreasing* grid bias and causing an increase in current flow through the tube. The increase in current flow across the cathode resistor causes a rising voltage which represents the output signal. This rising voltage, however, also has the effect of *increasing* grid bias because it makes the grid more negative with respect to the cathode.

The cathode follower circuit can also be adapted to a two input system such as shown at (B). Here, a dual-triode single envelope tube is employed. A signal applied to the No. 1 input or to the No. 2 input will appear across the common cathode resistor. Thus, this circuit forms a two input circuit known as a logical or-circuit of the type discussed more fully later.

The output impedance of a cathode follower is generally resistive, and is composed of a combination of the effective a-c resistance in parallel with the cathode resistance. The a-c resistance refers to the plate resistance (R_p) which is based on a change of plate voltage divided by a change in plate current, with grid voltage held constant. If the value of the cathode resistor and the plate resistance is known, the impedance (Z_0) of the cathode follower can be solved by the following formula:

$$Z_0 = \frac{R_p R_k}{R_p + R_k(\mu + 1)}$$

where R_p is a-c-plate resistance,

R_k is cathode resistance,

μ is rated amplification of tube.

The value of the cathode resistor (knowing the desired Z_0) is:

$$R_k = \frac{Z_0 R_p}{R_p - Z_0(\mu + 1)}$$

DELAY LINES

Delay lines are extensively used in digital computers for the purpose of delaying a pulse or a series of pulses for the duration of one or more pulses or for some other predetermined time interval. This delay procedure is necessary in some circuits which perform calculations involving addition, subtraction and multiplication as well as the storage devices as more fully explained later.

A delay line is any electronic circuit or device wherein a pulse which is applied to the input appears at the output at a later time interval. A delay line may be constructed from inductors and capacitors as shown in Fig. 2-19. Such a delay line will delay a pulse

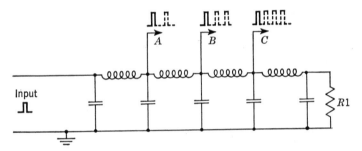

Fig. 2-19. Pulse delay line.

for a time interval as determined by the number of components of the delay line. When an input pulse is applied, it takes an appreciable time to charge the capacitors and for voltage to build up across them, as shown earlier in Fig. 1-8. In inductors, there is a lag in current build-up, and hence the combination of inductors and capacitors form the required delay as shown. The line may be tapped at various sections to secure the precise amount of delay required. For instance, if one pulse is applied to the input, it will appear at the output marked A at a time interval equal to the distance between pulses. Thus, the pulse output at A would represent a second place pulse as shown by the solid line instead of the first place pulse as indicated by the dotted line. The output from B would represent a third place pulse instead of the first place pulse applied to the input, again as shown by the solid line as compared to the dotted lines.

The output at C represents a three pulse delay, with the dotted outlines indicating the amount of delay encountered.

Delay lines are usually terminated by a load resistor equivalent to the surge impedance of the line. The surge impedance (Z) of the type of line illustrated is a function of the square root of the value of the inductance divided by the value of the capacitance:

$$Z = \sqrt{L/C}$$

The load resistor is necessary so that the energy which reaches the end of the line is absorbed and not reflected back as would be the case if the line were not terminated by a proper resistance. If no resistor were placed at the end of the line, the energy which reaches the end of the line would be reflected back again and would reappear, displaced in phase, at the various output terminals. This reflection process would produce undesired results, since there would be multiple pulse outputs for every pulse input at any given output terminal.

Sonic delay lines can also be employed. Sonic delay lines employ the principle of converting electric impulses to sound impulses. One method for doing this is to convert the electric impulses to sound impulses by use of a quartz crystal and then applying the sound pulses to a liquid such as oil or mercury. Sound travels through a liquid at a lower propagation rate than the rate at which electric pulses travel through wires and circuits, hence a delay is introduced. After the requisite delay has been established, the sound impulses are reconverted into electric impulses. The principles of this type of delay line are discussed more fully in Chapter 6.

BUFFER AMPLIFIERS

Often, the output from a flip-flop circuit must be connected to various other circuits. When such circuits are all connected to the output of a single flip-flop, the latter is loaded down to such an extent that its operation may be seriously impaired and become unreliable. Hence, the output of the flip-flop is isolated from other circuits by a buffer amplifier. A buffer amplifier is a basic amplifier, as described earlier. The high grid input impedance of the amplifier minimizes loading effects and hence acts as a good isolation between the flip-flop and the ultimate load represented by the stage which the flip-flop circuit feeds. Usually, the buffer amplifier is coupled to a cathode follower circuit and a clamper, as shown in Fig. 2-20, so that the output signal can be clamped at the correct

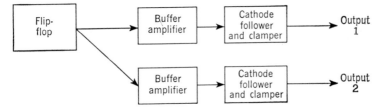

Fig. 2-20. Buffer amplifier applications.

amplitude level with a single polarity, either positive or negative, as desired.

While the cathode follower acts as a step-down device in similar fashion to a transformer, it does not diminish some of the frequency components of the signal as is often the case with a transformer. Buffer amplifier-cathode follower circuits are also used on occasion after a pulse delay line or in other cases where it is necessary to increase the amplitude of the signal to a proper level for use in the computers.

GAS TUBE CIRCUITS

Gas filled tubes are also found in computers because such tubes have low internal resistances and high current carrying capabilities. Symbols for the gas filled tubes are identical to the vacuum types except for a black dot denoting the presence of gas.

One application for the gas filled tube is in power supplies. The low internal resistance provides greater output and better regulation (the ability of the supply to maintain a constant voltage with variations in current drain). A typical full-wave power supply of this type is shown at (A) of Fig. 2-21. A radio-frequency choke (rfc) is used to filter out the noises generated by gas ionization. Sometimes the tube is housed in a perforated metal cage to shield other circuits from noise. With gas filled rectifier tubes, a choke input type of power supply is utilized to minimize arcing and also to improve regulation. The bleeder resistor also aids regulation by

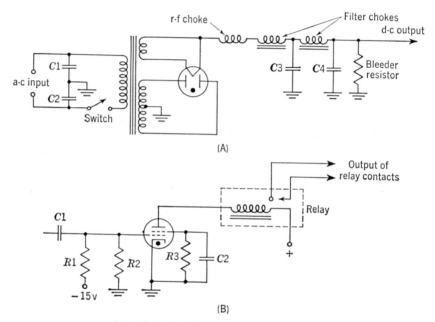

Fig. 2-21. Applications of gas tubes.

providing a small but constant current drain on the power supply, regardless of the external current drain of the computer circuits. Capacitors C1 and C2 filter the input system of the supply, preventing the entry of noises from the line.

Vacuum tube and selenium rectifier power supplies are also used in computer systems. The circuits are similar to that shown at (A) of Fig. 2-21 except for the absence of the radio frequency choke and, on occasion, use of capacitor instead of filter choke input.

Thyratron gas filled tubes are also employed besides the diode type previously discussed. The thyratrons have a control grid as well as shielding grids. The thyratron characteristic is such that the grid has control of the tube current flow during the time the gas is not ionized. Hence, during the nonionization state the grid can hold the tube at cut-off (no current flow) condition, if the grid is negative with respect to the cathode. When the negative potential is reduced to the point where it permits current flow within the tube, the electrons reach high velocity because of the attraction of the plus plate, and electrons are knocked off the gas atoms. When an atom has had an electron removed, it becomes an *ion* and has a plus charge. The gas atoms, having a plus charge, now also attract electrons from the cathode, and hence tube conduction reaches a maximum as soon as ionization occurs. During ionization, the grid loses control over tube current flow and is unable to produce cut-off even though the grid is made highly negative with respect to the cathode. Current flow must be interrupted by disconnection of the anode or cathode from the power supply.

Thyratrons can be used in generator applications and driver circuits, but not as amplifiers (because of lack of grid control once ionization occurs). A typical application for the thyratron in computer systems is the relay driver circuit illustrated at (B) of Fig. 2-21. Such a circuit is useful for actuating relays, since the thyratron has high current carrying capacities. (Relay applications are detailed in Chapter 7.)

Bias to the grid is applied by R1, with R2 providing a bleeding action for stability of the bias voltage. When the tube is nonconducting, no current flows through the relay coil and the relay contacts are open. Upon the application of a positive polarity pulse to the grid (of sufficient duration to permit ionization), the tube conducts heavily and the current flow through the relay coil sets up a strong magnetic field. The latter pulls down the relay contact armature, causing the relay switch to close. The switch will remain closed, even after the grid input signal pulse has left, because the tube will continue to conduct until the plate current is interrupted by opening the anode circuit. Vacuum tube relay drivers, when used, are similar in circuitry to that shown for the gas tube type.

TRANSISTORS

Since transistors perform all the various functions of vacuum tubes in terms of amplifying, generating, limiting, etc., they are extensively employed in computers. The advantages of transistors over vacuum tubes are the extremely small size of the former, low power consumption, long life, and the ability to handle well the type of signals encountered in computers. The primary disadvantage of the transistor is the inability to cope with as much power as vacuum tubes. Since computers, however, require thousands of circuits, the use of the transistor in computer circuitry means a considerable saving of space as well as a reduction in the costly power consumption encountered when thousands of vacuum tube circuits are used. In many instances where banks of vacuum tubes generate so much heat that air cooling blowers must be employed, transistor usage eliminates the necessity for such blowers, since the transistors operate at considerably lower power dissipation and hence at considerably lower temperatures.

In some instances, the transistors will also operate at much faster rates than vacuum tubes. The surface barrier transistor developed by Philco, for instance, is used in the TRANSAC digital computer and performs approximately 416,000 additions or subtractions a second. In multiplication the speed is also phenomenal, since two six-digit numbers such as 484,223 multiplied by 698,136 can be done in 48 microseconds. This speed is over 200,000 times faster than a similar calculation can be performed by a modern desk type calculator which would require over 10 seconds for procurement of the answer. Using a desk calculator, it would take over a day to perform 10,000 multiplications in series, while the TRANSAC digital computer would give answers at a rate exceeding 20,000 per second.

While such speed is extraordinarily faster than mechanical calculating machines, it is also at a somewhat faster rate than could be performed by vacuum tube computers, though the difference in speed between these two is only a ratio of about 10 to 1.

Transistors are miniature germanium or silicon crystal devices which perform as amplifiers, oscillators, switchers, and other circuits in similar fashion to vacuum tube applications. In contrast to the vacuum tube, however, the transistor requires no heated filament to produce controlled current flow. With the transistor, a steady-state current flow is established in the input and output circuits by the battery or power supply, and in the more common circuits the input has a much lower impedance than the output. In the amplifying process, an a-c signal is applied to the input and causes a variation in the input circuit current. Such a signal current variation causes a signal current variation in the output circuit. Depending on transistor type and circuit usage, the signal *current* change in the output circuit will have as great an amplitude as the input signal current changes. With some transistor circuits the current changes in the output circuit exceed the current changes which occur in the input circuit. Since the output impedance is higher than the input impedance, the signal current change of the output circuit develops a greater signal *power* than is applied to the input. Hence, power amplification is secured.

In a vacuum tube, the grid voltage is influential in regulating the amount of current flow in the anode circuit of the vacuum tube, while in a transistor the signal current which is established in the input circuit is the controlling factor. A variation of signal current in the input side overcomes certain barriers established within the transistor and hence amplification is possible. In oscillator circuits, appropriate feedback loops are employed so that the amplified signal energy is continuously fed to the input and such recycling causes the circuit to become self-sustaining with respect to signal circulation. Thus, a signal generator type of circuit is evolved. A comprehensive analysis of the theoretical factors involving transistor function are beyond the scope of this text. If a more thorough study of transistor function is desired, appropriate texts listed in the bibliography in the appendix should be consulted for the theory underlying current and hole flow in transistors, plus the formation of P-zones and N-zones. (These designations refer to positive [P] areas or zones with the transistor, and negative [N] areas or zones.)

Two basic transistors in common use are the P-N-P type and the N-P-N type. The P-N-P type indicates the transistor is composed of three sections, one a positive-zone (P-zone) section, another a negative-zone section, and an additional positive-zone section. When such sections are sandwiched together they form what is known as a *junction transistor*. A junction transistor can also be formed by sandwiching a P-section between two N-sections. Both types are illustrated in Fig. 2-22, at (A) and (B).

A P-N-P transistor can also be formed by fusing pigtail leads to a basic N-type slab. The fusion process creates positive zones and

such a transistor is known as a *point-contact* type, also illustrated in Fig. 2-22, at (C). The point-contact type transistor was the first type developed. It functions as an amplifier, oscillator, gate, etc.,

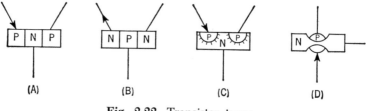

Fig. 2-22. Transistor types.

but has a high noise level and hence is undesirable for audio and radio frequency amplification purposes. The junction types, however, because of low noise level, are not only suitable for amplification purposes, but can also be used in switching and gating circuits and hence find extensive application in computer systems.

A third method for forming a P-N-P transistor is to fuse a certain element to an N-type crystal slab. This process is employed by RCA in its alloy junction transistor, and by Philco in its surface barrier transistor. Philco uses an etching process which is applied to two sides of the N-slab to form two concave sections. An electroplating process is then employed to deposit an element known as *indium* to the two concave sections to form P-zones. Such a transistor has low noise levels and is capable of operation at high frequencies in both amplifier and oscillator circuits. The surface barrier transistor is illustrated in Fig. 2-22 at (D). The schematic symbols for all types, whether junction, point contact, or surface barrier, are as shown in Fig. 2-23.

The transistor which is comparable to the *triode* vacuum tube has terminals called base, emitter, and collector. The emitter and collector terminals are those which are attached to the two similar zones. Thus, in a P-N-P transistor one P-zone would be attached to the collector terminal and the other P-zone to the emitter terminal. Similarly, in an N-P-N transistor, the emitter would be connected to one N-zone and the collector to the other N-zone. In either of the foregoing instances, the base connection is to the opposite zone section of the transistor.

The emitter terminal of a transistor is shown as an arrow connection to distinguish it from the collector. If the arrow is pointing toward the transistor, it indicates that the transistor is a P-N-P type,

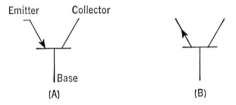

Fig. 2-23. Transistor symbols for P-N-P and N-P-N types.

and that the positive terminal of the battery or power supply must be applied (through the appropriate input resistance devices) to the emitter. The battery polarity applied to the collector is always opposite that of the emitter. Thus, in a P-N-P transistor, a negative polarity is applied to the collector (through the appropriate load resistor).

For an N-P-N transistor, the arrow lead indicating the emitter is drawn with the arrow pointing away from the emitter. Thus, an N-P-N transistor has a negative potential applied to the emitter N-section (through the appropriate coil or input resistor). The collector in an N-P-N transistor has a positive potential applied to it through the load resistor.

There are three basic methods for connecting a transistor into a circuit—the grounded base circuit, the grounded emitter circuit, and the grounded collector circuit.

The grounded base circuit is shown at (A) of Fig. 2-24, and if a P-N-P transistor is employed, the battery polarities would be as shown. The grounded base circuit for junction transistors has a low input impedance (less than 1,000 ohms) and a fairly high ouput impedance (up to 500,000 ohms). It functions well as an amplifier and is comparable to the grounded grid vacuum tube circuit. As with the latter, no phase reversal of signal occurs between input and output circuits of the grounded base amplifier.

The grounded emitter circuit shown at (B) of Fig. 2-24 has been extensively used in audio amplification as well as radio-frequency amplification systems, since it has more gain than the grounded base circuit and requires only one potential source for operation. It has a low input impedance (near 100 ohms) and the output impedance ranges up to 50,000 ohms. The grounded emitter

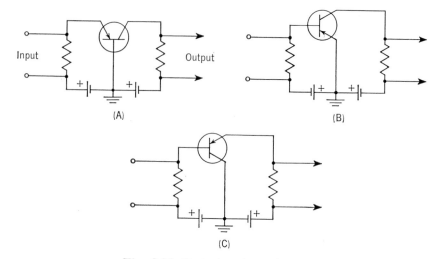

Fig. 2-24. Basic transistor circuitry.

circuit is comparable to the grounded cathode vacuum tube type, and there is a phase reversal of signal between input and output circuits. Gain is higher than the grounded base circuit, even though the output impedance is lower. Because of increased current gain, greater power amplification is achieved.

The grounded collector circuit shown at (C) of Fig. 2-24 has less than unity gain. Input impedance for junction types is high, often over 300,000 ohms, while output impedance is quite low, usually less than 100 ohms. It is comparable to the vacuum tube cathode follower circuit previously discussed; hence, it is utilized when it is necessary to employ a step-down device with a minimum of attenuation of wideband signal frequencies. As with the vacuum tube cathode follower, it is useful for terminating a series of circuits and feeding the output to a low impedance transmission line such as a coaxial cable. Since coaxial cables are extensively used between various sections of a complete electronic device, the cathode follower type circuit acts as an equivalent step-down transformer to convert a relatively high impedance to the low impedance of a coaxial cable transmission line, as with the tube type discussed earlier.

Besides amplifiers and cathode followers, transistors can be used in virtually all circuit applications that vacuum tubes can, including generators and flip-flop circuits. A multivibrator utilizing transistors is shown at (A) of Fig. 2-25, and resembles the vacuum tube type previously illustrated.

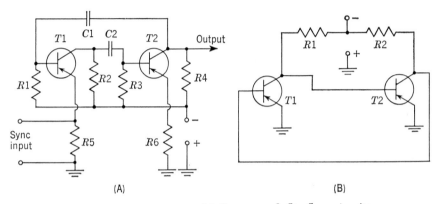

Fig. 2-25. Transistor multivibrator and flip-flop circuits.

Essentially, transistor $T1$ and transistor $T2$ are wired in a fashion similar to the grounded emitter amplifier. Capacitor $C1$ is the feedback capacitor which permits the circuit to function exactly as the vacuum tube type previously discussed. Base resistors have a high value, ranging up to 1 megohm, depending on the type of junction transistors utilized. Collector resistors range up to 10,000 ohms. The emitter resistor, $R5$, is of a low value (about 1,000 ohms) to provide for synchronization input without lifting the emitter too far above ground. Resistor $R6$ has the same value as $R5$ and is included to balance out the $T2$ circuit.

At (B) of Fig. 2-25 is shown the basic saturation flip-flop circuit used in the TRANSAC Digital Computer of the Philco Corporation. In this bistable circuit the conducting or "on" transistor has a base and collector current slightly more than 1 milliampere, while the "off" transistor base current will be about 5 microamperes and its collector current about 15 microamperes. The state of the circuit can be changed by applying a plus pulse to the base circuit of the "on" transistor.

If $T1$ is at saturation, its collector voltage is low enough to cut off $T2$. If a pulse is applied to the base of $T1$ then $T1$ is cut off and collector voltage (negative) rises. This voltage, directly coupled to the base of $T2$, permits the latter to go into conduction, developing a large voltage drop across $R2$, and lowering the $T2$ collector voltage. This voltage is applied to the base of $T1$, holding the latter at cut-off until another input pulse is applied to the circuit.

Transistor circuits making up calculating elements in computers are widely utilized, as more fully described later. In general, however, transistor circuits operate in a fashion similar to their vacuum tube counterparts. Hence, the explanations of the functional aspects of computer circuitry using tubes apply as well to such circuits utilizing transistors.

While the transistors utilized in computers and other electronic devices are incapable of handling the high power which can be handled by vacuum tubes, transistors are undergoing a continual development and many modern types are capable of providing an output of sufficient wattage to provide for virtually all the uses in normal audio, r-f, switching, and generating circuits. In push-pull arrangements the power transistors can deliver more than twice the normal wattage of a single transistor and hence power outputs in excess of 10 or more watts are not uncommon.

OTHER BISTABLE DEVICES

Devices other than vacuum tubes or transistors can be used to design bistable circuits. One such device is the *ferrite core* illustrated at (A) of Fig. 2-26. The ferrite core can be magnetized in a fashion similar to a bar magnet. Thus, the core can be magnetized in one direction to represent an "on" state (1) or in the other direction for the "off" state (0). If the first ferrite core ($F1$) is in the *on* state, and the second ($F2$) is in the *off* state, a pulse applied to the input of $F1$ will cause current to flow through $L1$ and, if the polarity is correct, will reverse the state of *F1*. In reversing, *F1* induces a voltage across *L2* and current will circulate through *L2* and *L3*. Current through *L3* will change the *off* state of *F2* and produce an output voltage across *L4*. Winding *L3* has fewer turns

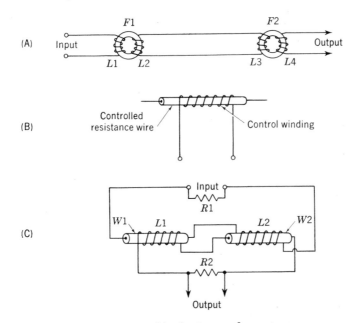

Fig. 2-26. Bistable ferrites and cryotrons.

on it than *L2*, to prevent the re-flipping of *F1* as *F2* flips over. Diodes can also be used to prevent reverse transfer of signals. Thus, an imput pulse to *F1* flips over the latter and transfers the output signal to *F2*, also flipping over this core and producing an output. (For basic theory involving ferrite cores, see Chapter 6, Storage Systems.)

Another bistable device is the *cryotron*. The operation of this device is based on the superconductivity of certain metals near zero temperature. The normal resistance exhibited by such metals at normal temperatures disappears near zero temperature and hence the metals become superconductors of electric current. The conductivity can be altered, however, by the application of a magnetic field. The latter can shift the resistive characteristics of the metal from superconductivity to its normal resistive state as the magnetic field is kept low, or raised to a higher level. Thus, a bistable characteristic is achieved.

The basic cryotron is shown at (B) of Fig. 2-26. The horizontal straight wire (about 1 inch long) is the equivalent of the anode in a vacuum tube and represents the resistance to be controlled. The coil around the center wire is the control winding and is equivalent to the control grid of a vacuum tube. The control winding consists of several hundred turns of very fine insulated wire. A small current change in the control winding can change the magnetic fields sufficiently to control comparatively large currents in the center wire. Hence, the device also has amplifying characteristics. For operation, the various cryotron circuits must be kept at extremely low temperatures, necessitating use of refrigeration processes. The over-all compactness of the cryotron circuits, however, means small computer units despite the added space needed for the refrigerating unit.

The cryotron principle applied to a basic flip-flop circuit is shown at (C) of Fig. 2-26. Assume the current through $L1$ is low and only a small magnetic field is created. Current through the center wire ($W1$) would be high, since the center metal is at superconductivity. The high current through the center wire ($W1$) is also flowing through $L2$, because the latter is in series with $W1$; a high magnetic field exists around $L2$, and the center wire $W2$ is kept from superconductivity by this field. Wire $W2$ thus has a normal resistance (and reduced current flow). The reduced current flow through $W2$ corresponds to the reduced current through $L1$, which is in series with $W2$. Thus, $W1$ is in a high conducting state, while the second center wire $W2$ is at low conduction. Wires $W1$ and $W2$ therefore represent two stable states. The high current through $W1$ and $L2$ also flows through the output resistor $R2$, producing a large voltage drop.

If a pulse of proper polarity is now applied to the input, the pulse will oppose the direction of current flow through the input resistor $R1$, and current flow will be reduced. The reduction of current through $L2$ reduces the magnetic fields of the latter and permits $W2$ to go into superconductivity with increased current flow.

Coil $L1$, in series with $W2$, also has a current increase and the magnetic fields build up and cause $W1$ to change from superconductivity to normal resistivity. Thus, each cryotron has changed from one stable state to another. The change of state will produce an output pulse across $R2$.

Questions Relating to Chapter 2

1. Briefly explain what is meant by a *bistable* circuit.

2. Explain why a cathode resistor used for bias purposes is unable to provide cut-off bias.

3. Draw a flip-flop circuit and indicate which tube is at saturation and which tube at conduction after the circuit is turned on. Also show where a triggering voltage can be applied to change the tube which is at cut-off so that it is operating at saturation.

4. *a*) What type of oscillator generates sinewaves?
   b) What type of oscillator generates square waves?
   c) Explain how a cathode coupled multivibrator differs from a plate coupled type.

5. Explain the essential differences between a single shot multivibrator and the cathode coupled multivibrator.

6. Draw a series diode clipping circuit with positive signal output and briefly explain its operation. Repeat for a shunt clipper circuit.

7. Reproduce a drawing of a discharge circuit and briefly explain its operation.

8. *a*) Draw a basic cathode follower circuit.
   b) What is a useful function of a cathode follower?
   c) Why is voltage gain less than unity in a cathode follower?

9. *a*) What is the purpose for a delay line in digital computers?
   b) How is the surge impedance of a line calculated?
   c) What is the purpose of a load resistor for termination of a delay line?

10. Briefly explain what is meant by a buffer amplifier.

11. *a*) How does the control grid function of a thyratron differ from that of an ordinary vacuum tube?
    b) Explain the basic operation of a relay driver.

12. List three advantages of transistors over vacuum tubes in the design of digital computers, and give one disadvantage of a transistor over a vacuum tube.

13. If an N-P-N transistor is utilized in a grounded base amplifier circuit, what must be the battery polarity to the collector and the polarity to the emitter? To what vacuum tube circuit is the grounded base comparable?

14. If a P-N-P transistor is employed in a grounded emitter amplifier circuit, what must be the polarity of the voltage applied to the emitter and the polarity of the voltage applied to the collector? To what vacuum tube circuit is the grounded emitter comparable?

15. Reproduce a transistorized flip-flop circuit and briefly explain its operation.

3 □ □ ■
□ □ □
□ □ □

COMPUTER ARITHMETIC
APPLICATIONS

BINARY COUNTING

Before a discussion is undertaken regarding the manner in which a series of flip-flop circuits perform counting functions, it is necessary to consider in greater detail how arithmetic functions are applied to circuit conditions of saturation and cut-off. In a device having two stable states, representation of the states is limited only to the symbol 0 (an "off" condition) and the symbol 1 (an "on" condition). The method by which these two representations are utilized in the complex addition, subtraction, and multiplication processes can be more clearly understood by initially reviewing the simple desk type adding machine illustrated in Fig. 3-1.

In such a simple adding machine, the wheel on the right designated as R, represents the units or first place digits. When this wheel is turned one-tenth rotation to the right, the number 1 appears below the arrow indicating that the machine has "stored" the numeral 1 and is ready to add another number to it. Successive turns will increase the number beneath the arrow until number 9 is reached. On the next one-tenth turn, the wheel returns to 0 but in doing so an internal trip lever turns the second wheel (M)

one-tenth turn. The middle wheel thus indicates the tens, and it would take another complete revolution of wheel *R* to cause wheel *M* to turn one-tenth turn to complete twenty. A complete revolution of wheel *M* will trip wheel *L* one-tenth turn to register

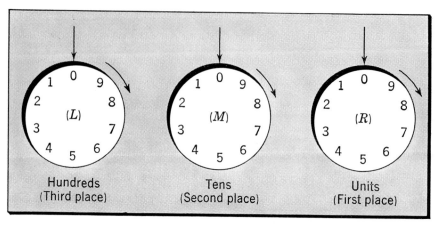

Fig. 3-1. Simple adding machine.

the numeral 1, which, in the third place from the right, represents hundreds. This is the basic decimal system we utilize, since we have only ten digits (0 to 9), and the symbols used for these numbers are Arabic. As mentioned in Chapter 1 (Introduction), the reason for only ten digits in our decimal system probably has its origin in the early days of civilization. At that time, when man first found it expedient to count, he utilized his fingers as the reference for indicating one, two, or more items up to ten. Since only ten symbols are used we exhaust our stock of identifying symbols after counting from 0 to 9. Thus, in order to indicate a larger number, initial symbols must be repeated by combining them.

Symbol systems other than the Arabic exist, however, such as the Roman numeral system, still utilized on some clocks as well as in some published works (such as in the preface numbering and appendix numbering of books). The Roman numeral system utilizes the letters of the alphabet wherein the letter I represents 1, V equals 5, and X equals 10. In the Roman numeral system a representation of 2 involves the placing of an additional I beside the original I, and 3 is represented by placing an additional I beside the two I's. Once the next highest order symbol was reached (V) an additional letter I was used to indicate 6, as VI, and for 7 an additional letter I was placed beside it, VII, etc.

The decimal system with a base ten is not the only one which could be employed for arithmetical purposes. Systems with a base five or even a base fifteen can, in principle, be employed. An extremely useful system for digital computers is one using the base two, utilizing only the two symbols 0 and 1, and known as binary arithmetic. Each digit is called a *bit* and use of the 0 and 1 symbols is known as *binary* notation.

The number of digits employed in a numbering system is known as *radix*. Thus, *radix ten* (0 to 9) designates the ordinary decimal system commonly in use. A *radix two* refers to the binary number system which utilizes two numbers, 0 and 1. A radix eight and a radix sixteen have, on occasion, been used to a limited extent for some computers, but the radix two system is the most suitable for digital computer application.

The manner in which a system using only two identifying digits can be set up as an adding machine is shown in Fig. 3-2. Here

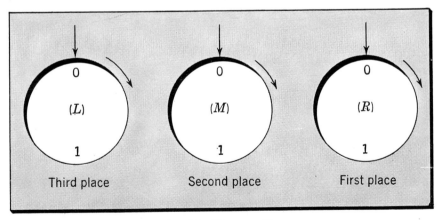

Fig. 3-2. Binary adder.

again are three wheels, *R*, *M*, and *L*. As before, the progression is from right to left in *accumulating* the results of additive digits. In the case shown, however, each wheel has only a 0 and a 1 on it. Instead of each wheel rotating one-tenth turn to indicate the addition of the numeral 1, each wheel rotates *one-half turn* to indicate the insertion of the numeral 1. Thus, for the beginning of the addition, each wheel would be set as shown in Fig. 3-2, representing 0. When 1 is to be added to another number, the R wheel on the right is turned one-half turn and the numeral 1 appears below the arrow to indicate the *registering* of this number. The numeral 1 representation is similar to the base ten adder previously mentioned, but the addition of other numbers changes the "answers" appearing under the arrows to a considerable degree as compared with the decimal system. If, for instance, the R wheel were turned another one-half turn to indicate the insertion of another digit, it would trip wheel M and cause it to rotate one-half turn. The process is illustrated at (A) of Fig. 3-3 where the right wheel (R) indicates the numeral 1 beneath the arrow while the middle wheel (M) and the left wheel (L) indicate 0's. If another digit 1 is to be added to the 1 now stored in the machine, the right wheel would be rotated another one-half turn. This would cause the middle wheel to rotate one-half turn also and register 1. The right wheel, however, returns to 0 as shown at (B) of Fig. 3-3. Now, only the center

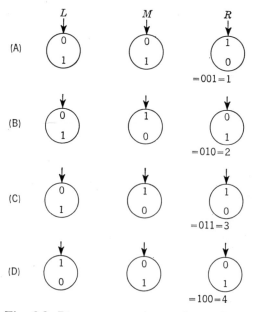

Fig. 3-3. Binary process in simple machine.

wheel registers a 1 but in this device the sum under the arrows (010) represents the decimal number 2. If another digit is to be added to the sum now stored in the machine, the wheel at the right would be made to rotate another half turn and the numeral 1 would appear under the arrow as shown at (C). Since, however, it takes a full revolution of the R wheel to turn the M wheel one-half turn, the M wheel is not tripped during this operation but remains with the numeral 1 beneath the arrow. Hence, the machine now registers 011 which represents 3 in our base ten decimal system.

To carry the illustration farther, assume that another digit is to be added to the stored number of the machine. In such an instance the right wheel would be rotated another one-half turn which would bring the 0 of this wheel under the arrow, as shown at (D). Now, however, the R wheel will cause the M wheel to rotate one-half turn bringing the 0 of the latter to the top. Since the M wheel has now made a complete revolution, it trips the L wheel at the left one-half turn and registers the number 1 of this wheel under the arrow. Now the machine indicates 100 and this represents 4 in our base ten decimal system. The addition of another number would cause the left wheel to indicate 1 and hence the machine would register 101 which would equal 5 in our decimal system. If a number of such wheels were utilized, a large sum of numbers could be added just as is the case with the decimal type of adding machine shown in Fig. 3-1. The numbers represented by the wheels are binary numbers and the process of utilizing such numbers is known as binary notation.

The chart shown in Fig. 3-4 represents the decimal numbers indicated by the numerals appearing on the wheels. Five possible wheels are shown and the wheel positions also indicate the "place" of the numerals from right to left in the binary system. The decimal count to twenty is given, though this is not the limit of a five place counter. For practice purposes, however, the binary notation should be completed by the reader up to the limit of the numbers which can be indicated by the five place device.

You will note that in the first place column the numeral 1 alternates with 0 all the way down the column. In the second place column, two 0's alternate with two 1's all the way down the column. In the third place column four 0's alternate with four 1's all the way down the column, etc.

| | Decimal |
Wheel Position: 5 4 3 2 1	Sum
Wheel Registration: 0 0 0 0 0 =	0
0 0 0 0 1 =	1
0 0 0 1 0 =	2
0 0 0 1 1 =	3
0 0 1 0 0 =	4
0 0 1 0 1 =	5
0 0 1 1 0 =	6
0 0 1 1 1 =	7
0 1 0 0 0 =	8
0 1 0 0 1 =	9
0 1 0 1 0 =	10
0 1 0 1 1 =	11
0 1 1 0 0 =	12
0 1 1 0 1 =	13
0 1 1 1 0 =	14
0 1 1 1 1 =	15
1 0 0 0 0 =	16
1 0 0 0 1 =	17
1 0 0 1 0 =	18
1 0 0 1 1 =	19
1 0 1 0 0 =	20

Fig. 3-4. Binary vs. decimal numbers.

The binary system is based on the powers of 2 and each power of 2 which a place represents can be set down as follows:

	8	7	6	5	4	3	2	1	←Place
etc.	2^7	2^6	2^5	2^4	2^3	2^2	2^1	2^0	←Power
	128	64	32	16	8	4	2	1	←Value

The foregoing table is useful for ascertaining the decimal equivalent of a binary sum. If, for instance, the decimal equivalent of the binary number 111 were desired, reference to the foregoing table indicates the first digit has a value of 1, the second digit a value of 2, and the third digit a value of 4. The decimal sum is then equivalent to:

$$1 \quad 1 \quad 1$$
$$4 + 2 + 1 = 7$$

In utilizing this method, however, it must be remembered that 0's in *any* place cancel out the value such a place would have. Thus, if the decimal equivalent of the binary number 1010 were needed, reference to the table indicates that the fourth place digit represents 8 and the second place digit represents 2. Hence, the resultant decimal sum is indicated as follows:

$$1 \ 0 \ 1 \ 0$$
$$8 + 2 = 10$$

In this manner, any sum in binary notation can be converted to its base ten (decimal) equivalent by reference to the powers of 2 table shown above. Another example will help in understanding the process involved:

Binary sum: 1 0 1 0 1 0 0
Value: $64 + 16 + \ 4 \quad = 84$

BINARY ADDITION

Binary numbers can be added in similar fashion to the addition employed in the decimal system. If, for instance, the binary number 11 (3) were to be added to the binary number 100 (4) the numbers will be added together in simple fashion as shown below to give the binary sum of 111. Reference to the table in Fig. 3-4 indicates that this binary number equals 7 and thus proves the addition.

$$
\begin{array}{r}
11 \ (3) \quad \text{addend} \\
+100 \ (4) \quad \text{augend} \\
\hline
111 \ (7) \quad \text{sum}
\end{array}
$$

In binary arithmetic, however, the addition process requires the "carrying" of a number just as it does with the decimal system addition. If, for instance, we added 01 to 101 it would be set down as follows:

$$
\begin{array}{r}
01 \\
+101 \\
\end{array}
$$

The addition of the two digits in the first place column would represent the decimal number 2; but since the numeral 1 is our highest number in the binary system we must set down a 0 for the *sum* of

1 and 1, just as we set down a 0 in the first place if we have reached the highest order of our decimal number 9 and are adding another 1 to it. After setting down the 0 we carry 1 to the second place and therefore the binary sum would be 110 as shown below.

$$\begin{array}{r} {}^1 01 \\ +101 \\ \hline 110 \end{array}$$

Proof of this addition can be obtained by reference to the table since 01 equals 1 and 101 equals 5 and the sum of these equals 6 (110).

Sometimes it is necessary to carry more than a single digit as represented by the following example:

$$\begin{array}{r} {}^1 1_0\, 1 \\ 1\ 1_0 \\ {}^{11}1\ 0\ 1 \\ \hline 1\ 0\ 1\ 1 \end{array}$$

Here, we would start with the top first place digit and add this to the next column first place digit which gives us 0 and 1 to carry. The remaining 1 in the bottom row plus the 0 resulting from the addition of the first place digits would equal 1, and hence the numeral 1 is placed below the first place column as shown. In the second place column the 1 which carried plus the top 1 equals 0 with 1 to carry. Zero plus 1 in the second column would equal 1, and this is set down below as shown. In the third place vertical column the 1 which was carried plus the 1 in the column equals 0 with 1 to carry. When the 1 which is carried is placed in the answer, the resultant binary sum equals 1011 which represents 11 in the decimal system. Since the binary numbers which were added are represented in decimal system addition as 3 plus 3 plus 5, the true sum has been obtained by the addition of the binary numbers.

BINARY SUBTRACTION

Binary numbers can also be subtracted from other binary numbers in a fashion similar to that employed in the decimal system. If, for instance, the binary number 11 is to be subtracted from 111 the operation would be as follows:

$$
\begin{array}{ll}
111 \ (7) & \text{minuend} \\
-11 \ (3) & \text{subtrahend} \\
\hline
100 \ (4) & \text{remainder}
\end{array}
$$

The foregoing is a simple illustration, since the digit 1 is subtracted from another digit just as in the decimal system. As with the latter, however, it is necessary to "borrow" a number from the next place when the number in the minuend is smaller than the number in the subtrahend. This is shown in the following example where the binary number 01 is to be subtracted from the binary number 110:

$$
\begin{array}{ll}
110 & (6) \\
-01 & (1) \\
\hline
101 & (5)
\end{array}
$$

Since the numeral 1 in the subtrahend is a larger number than the 0 in the minuend above it, one numeral is borrowed from the second place. (The second place numeral 1 plus the 0 in first place represent 2.) The subtraction of the first place numeral 1 from the minuend therefore equals 1. The second place subtraction indicates a 0 which is to be subtracted from the minuend number. Since the second place minuend was borrowed, however, it represents 0, and hence the subtraction gives the remainder as the binary number 101 as shown above. As with the decimal system, borrowing from second and third place is also necessary as shown below:

$$
\begin{array}{ll}
1000 \ (8) \qquad & 1000 \ (8) \\
-11 \ (3) & -111 \ (7) \\
\hline
101 \ (5) & 0001 \ (1)
\end{array}
$$

BINARY MULTIPLICATION

Multiplication with binary numbers can also be performed as with the decimal system. If, for instance, the binary number of 101 (5) is to be multiplied by 11 (3), the multiplicand is set down once to represent the first order multiplier and then is set down again but displaced to the left by one place to indicate the second place multiplier function. Addition of these two (known as partial products) is then performed as in regular multiplication problems.

The result is the binary number 1111, representing the decimal equivalent 15 as shown below:

$$
\begin{array}{rll}
101 & (5) & \text{multiplicand} \\
\times 11 & (3) & \text{multiplier} \\
\hline
101 & \\
101 & \Big\}} & \text{partial products} \\
\hline
1111 & (15) & \text{product}
\end{array}
$$

If the multiplier has a 0 in it, the 0's may be set down as in the example shown below. The same problem given above is used for the example, except that the multiplicand and multiplier numbers have been interchanged.

$$
\begin{array}{r}
11 \\
\times 101 \\
\hline
11 \\
00 \\
11 \\
\hline
1111
\end{array}
$$

As the following example indicates, in some instances it will be necessary to employ the "carry" principle in the addition process just as would be the case in high numbers involving the decimal system. In the following multiplication of 111 (7) by 11 (3) the decimal sum of 21 is indicated by the binary sum 10101 as shown.

$$
\begin{array}{r}
1\,1\,1 \\
\times 1\,1 \\
\hline
{}^{1}1_{0}1\,1 \\
{}^{1}1\,1\,1 \\
\hline
1\,0\,1\,0\,1 = 16 + 4 + 1 = 21
\end{array}
$$

BINARY DIVISION

Division can also be employed, and the problem becomes quite simple when first or second place 0's are involved, since such 0's can be canceled just as in the decimal system. A simple example is shown below, where the binary number 1100 is to be divided by 100. Crossing off the end 0's indicates the quotient to be 11 (3), which is the correct answer.

$$
\begin{array}{l}
\text{dividend} \\
\text{divisor}
\end{array}
\quad
\frac{1100\ (12)}{100\ (\ 4)} = 11\ (3) \quad \text{quotient}
$$

A more complex type of division occurs when the binary number 1110 is to be divided by 11, or the binary number 10010 is to be divided by 110. Both examples are shown below:

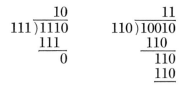

$$
\begin{array}{r}
10 \\
111\overline{)1110} \\
111 \\
\hline
0
\end{array}
\qquad
\begin{array}{r}
11 \\
110\overline{)10010} \\
110 \\
\hline
110 \\
110
\end{array}
$$

In the second example shown above, the binary number 110 is larger than the first three digits in the dividend (100), hence the division process must embrace that portion of the dividend represented by 1001 which follows the general rule in decimal divisions.

The divisor, 110, "goes into" the 1001 portion of the dividend and hence is set below it as shown. When 110 is subtracted from 1001 by binary subtraction, the resultant is 11. When the last 0 in the dividend is then brought down, the result is 110 which means that the divisor can go into this number once, and when this is indicated in the quotient the proper answer (11) is derived. The latter problem, converted to the decimal system, involves dividing 18 by 6 to provide a quotient of 3, as reference to the previous table will indicate.

The foregoing discussion of binary notation, decimal coding, etc. has been given to familiarize the reader with the processes involved in digital computers. The actual calculations involving binary numbers or other codes are, of course, done by the computer electronically during time intervals incredibly short in comparison with the time it would take to do such calculations by the most proficient of mathematicians. The conversion of one code to another is also handled internally by the computer, one code being entered into certain circuits, and the manner of tapping off the information from the circuits done in such a manner as to provide the conversion process of changing one code into another. Despite the automatic handling of the mathematical processes by the computer itself, an understanding of binary notation and its allied coding is of great value. Such knowledge aids in understanding the actual calculation processes performed in the computer, and enables the reader to grasp the manner in which circuit combinations perform the various functions of multiplication, division, etc., as more fully explained later. A knowledge of the arithmetic principles is also of considerable help in the maintenance and trouble shooting procedures involved with digital computers. Hence, the foregoing examples should be studied carefully and additional problems worked out as an aid to becoming thoroughly familiar with both the system of binary notation and the auxiliary codes discussed herein. With a solid foundation in the principles given in the foregoing parts of this chapter and in earlier chapters, the reader will have no difficulty in analyzing the counter systems discussed in the remainder of this chapter as well as the more complex systems detailed in subsequent chapters.

BINARY-CODED DECIMAL

Not all computers confine themselves exclusively to the binary numbering system. There are cases when the decimal system is used in the actual computer circuitry, one typical example being the decade counter, discussed later. Because the computer circuitry operates on the "on" and "off" conditions, however, it is necessary to convert decimal numbers into the type of notation which can be handled by the computer. The most convenient way for doing this is to use binary notation to express the decimal numbers. When this is done, each decimal number is coded in terms of a binary number, and hence the system is known as *binary-coded decimal.*

The coding can consist of any system desired, though the most logical procedure would be to code each decimal digit by a binary number which would express the equivalent figure. Thus, the decimal number 2 would be expressed as 10, and the decimal number 3 would be expressed as 11, etc.

In coding decimal numbers in this fashion, the first nine digits of the decimal system would be expressed in the binary number representing such a figure, just as was shown in the table of Fig. 3-4. After the ninth number, however, the binary-coded decimal notation would differ, since it is expedient to conform to the decimal notation system by repeating, after the first nine numbers, the same coded symbols used earlier. This is illustrated in the table shown below. Note that the decimal number 12, for instance, is represented by the number 1, followed by the binary number 2:

Decimal Number		Binary-Coded		
01		0001		
02		0010		
03		0011		
04		0100		
05		0101		
	etc.			
09		1001		
10		0001	0000	
11		0001	0001	
12		0001	0010	
13		0001	0011	
	etc.			
20		0010	0000	
21		0010	0001	
22		0010	0010	
23		0010	0011	
	etc.			
364		0011	0110	0100
365		0011	0110	0101
	etc.			

In using the above system it will be noticed that four binary bits are required for each decimal digit, because the largest decimal number (9) is expressed as 1001. The binary-coded decimal system is also useful with a computer which utilizes the binary system internally. By using the binary-coded decimal for placing information into the computer or taking it out, greater convenience in operation may often be achieved. A basic output (read-out) method consists of vertical rows of lights such as shown in Fig. 3-5, to indicate the decimal equivalent of the binary-coded decimal number. As shown in Fig. 3-5, the first place lights in the vertical row at the right read 3, because the lights representing 1 and 2 are both lit. Note that the binary place is represented vertically, starting from the bottom, while the decimal place is represented horizontally, starting from the right. The second place column reads 6, etc. to give a total number of 8563.

A variation of the binary-coded decimal notation is one known as the *excess-three code*. In this system, each decimal digit is coded

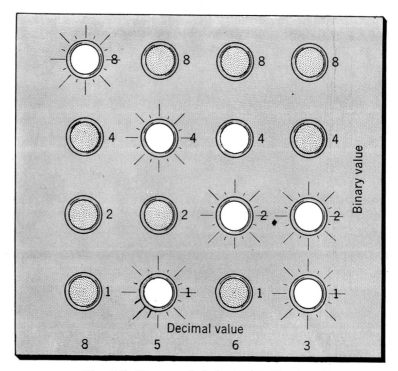

Fig. 3-5. Binary-coded decimal indication.

in binary, except that three (011) is added to the number formed by the binary coding. The following table indicates this method of notation:

Decimal Number	Excess-Three Code
00	0011
01	0100
02	0101
03	0110
04	0111
05	1000
06	1001
07	1010
08	1011
09	1100

The excess-three code is useful in simplifying subtraction processes in digital computers because of the characteristic complement of nine for each pair of related digits. You will note from

the foregoing table that the 0 and the 9 are symbolic opposites—
that is, 0011 and 1100. In the decimal number 0, the excess-three
code has the 0 where the 1's are, in the excess-three code equivalent
for the decimal number 9. In this case, the 0 replaces the 1 and
vice versa. This factor also holds for the numbers 3 and 6, wherein
the 3 is expressed as 0110 and the 6 is expressed as 1001. The decimal numbers 2 and 7 also are symbolic opposites, indicated as 0101
and 1010. Numbers 4 and 5 also have directly opposite characteristics because the 4 is expressed as 0111 and the 5 is expressed as
1000. This complementing feature means that any number subtracted from 9 indicates the remainder by simply interchanging the
0's and 1's in the number to be subtracted. For instance, if 2 is to
be subtracted from 9, the excess-three code for 2 is 0101. Replacing the 0's with 1's and the 1's with 0's in the latter number gives
us 1010 which equals 7 in the excess-three code. Thus, by interchanging 0's and 1's in the number which was to be subtracted, we
immediately arrive at the remainder. The following is an additional
example to help illustrate this process:

Decimal Number		Excess-Three
9	=	1100
−4	=	0111
5	=	1000

Another code which is useful is that known as the 7,4,2,1 code.
This code has been devised in order to minimize the number of 1's
in the code group. In this system simplification is procured because
the number of 1's in any code group is limited to two. In the pure
binary system, the value of the first place digit is 1, the second
place 2, the third place 4, the fourth place 8. Hence, the binary
system is sometimes referred to as the 1,2,4,8 system (or 8,4,2,1).
In the 7,4,2,1 system, the fourth place digit has a value of 7 as shown
in the column below. This code reduces electric energy consumption because of the reduction in the number of pulses which must
be applied for a particular number or numbers, and is also more
convenient with respect to input systems such as punched cards.
This code, and all the decimal symbols, are given as follows:

Decimal Number	7,4,2,1 Code
0	0000
1	0001
2	0010
3	0011
4	0100
5	0101
6	0110
7	1000
8	1001
9	1010

GRAY CODE

Another form of coding which finds practical application is that known as the *Gray* code. It is particularly useful with respect to converting a given mechanical change into an equivalent numerical expression. Hence, the Gray code is used to indicate a prescribed movement of a shaft or to indicate any other variable function and express it numerically, as in analog computers (see Chapter 1). To facilitate the coding of a small variable with regard to a number expressed in a given code, it is desirable to change only one digit at a time when going from one number to the next highest number. This also adds greater accuracy in the design of some units, because in pure binary notation there are instances where several digits change during the numerical progress. For instance, in binary, when changing from the number 3 (0011) to 4 (0100), three digits must change since the two digits in 0011 must revert to 0's and the third place 0 must be changed to a 1. Similarly, going from 7 (0111) to 8 (1000) involves a change of four digits. From 15 (1111) to 16 (10000) involves a change of five digits. Operational errors are reduced considerably if only one digit at a time changes as the numerical value increases. The Gray code (sometimes called *cyclic code*) is such a system. The following table indicates the Gray code equivalent of decimal numbers up to 12.

Decimal Number	Pure Binary	Gray Code
0	0000	0000
1	0001	0001

Decimal Number	Pure Binary	Gray Code
2	0010	0011
3	0011	0010
4	0100	0110
5	0101	0111
6	0110	0101
7	0111	0100
8	1000	1100
9	1001	1101
10	1010	1111
11	1011	1110
12	1100	1010

An inspection of the foregoing table will indicate the technique used to obtain the Gray code. To convert a binary number to its Gray code equivalent, the binary number is added to itself without carrying, but the added number *is indexed (moved over) to the right by one place, dropping the digit which would extend beyond the original number.* Thus, to express the binary number 2 (10) in Gray code, the process is:

$$\begin{array}{l} 10 \quad \text{(Binary 2)} \\ \underline{+1} \quad \text{(Binary 2 indexed to right by one number)} \\ 11 \end{array}$$

When a carry function is indicated, it is ignored. The following indicates this process, where the number 6 (110) is converted to the Gray code:

$$\begin{array}{l} 110 \quad (6) \\ \underline{+11} \quad (6 \text{ indexed}) \\ 101 \quad \text{Gray code 6} \end{array}$$

Note in the foregoing that in second place the addition of 1 plus 1 equals 0 with one to carry. In converting to the Gray code, however, the carry function is not performed. This holds true even though a number of digits would be resolved, such as the following indicates:

$$\begin{array}{l} 1111 \quad (15) \\ \underline{+111} \quad (15 \text{ indexed}) \\ 1000 \quad \text{Gray Code 15} \end{array}$$

FLOATING DECIMAL POINT

Floating decimal point operation in a computer refers to the processes employed for taking short cuts with respect to computer arithmetic. The floating decimal point method of notation permits the storage of the power of 10 plus the multiplier, instead of storing the entire number including all the digits represented by such a number. The power of 10 which is stored acts to locate the decimal point of the number, and hence assures an automatic placement of the decimal point for arithmetic operations.

The floating decimal point principles had long been employed by engineers in normal calculations before the advent of computers. The system has been variously designated as *scientific notation, engineers shorthand, etc.* The method consists of expressing the number as one having a value less than 10, and then multiplying the number by 10 for as many times as required for proper location of the decimal point. The multiplier is expressed exponentially. For example, 10^2 indicates that 10 is to be multiplied by itself; 10^3 indicates that the multiplication involves 10 times 10 times 10 which equals 1,000. Thus, 1,300 can be expressed as 1.3 times 10^3 or 0.13 times 10^4, etc. In the foregoing, the 1.3 times 10^3 simply means 1.3 times 1,000 which of course equals 1,300.

A partial table showing powers of 10 and the exponents is shown below. This table can be extended for higher exponents by simply adding a 0 to successive figures in the right hand column:

$$10^0 = 1$$
$$10^1 = 10$$
$$10^2 = 100$$
$$10^3 = 1,000$$
$$10^4 = 10,000$$
$$10^5 = 100,000$$
etc.

Not only are large numbers written in reduced form by this method, but arithmetic operations are also simplified. In multiplication, for instance, 1,300 times 1,300 equals 1,690,000. Using the floating decimal point notation, however, all numbers are multiplied and the exponents of 10 are added. Hence, the foregoing example would be:

$$(1.3)(10^3) \text{ times } (1.3)(10^3)$$

This would equal $1.69(10^6)$ which is 1,690,000. Note that the exponents are added. The floating decimal point system eliminates the need for adding many columns as is done in the conventional multiplication processes wherein partial products are employed, etc. Powers of 10 can also have negative exponents as shown by the table below:

$$10^{-1} = 0.1$$
$$10^{-2} = 0.01$$
$$10^{-3} = 0.001$$
$$10^{-4} = 0.0001$$
$$10^{-5} = 0.00001$$

etc.

The negative exponents permit the writing of large fractional numbers in simplified form and again help locate the decimal point. For instance, 0.0000057 equals 5.7 times 10^{-6}.

ERROR-DETECTING CODES

Another type of code is that which is specifically designed for detecting any errors which might occur. Such codes are particularly useful where punched cards or perforated tape is employed for feeding information into the computer. The most common method for establishing a particular error-detecting code is the use of only two "1" digits plus three 0's for numbers from 0 to 9. By keeping the number of pulses which represent 1's to a minimum there is less chance for error. If the coding is such that only two 1's are employed in conjunction with three 0's, any number with only two 0's or four 0's is incorrect. The following is an example of such a code:

$$0 = 00011$$
$$1 = 00110$$
$$2 = 01100$$
$$3 = 11000$$
$$4 = 10001$$
$$5 = 10010$$
$$6 = 10100$$
$$7 = 01010$$
$$8 = 00101$$
$$9 = 01001$$

There are various combinations of three 0's and two 1's which can be employed for coding a series of numbers from 0 to 9, and the particular one employed in a computer may be different from the one shown above. If desired, the designer can employ 11000 to represent the number 1, 10001 for 2, 10010 for 3, etc. This type of code is sometimes called the "two-out-of-five" code because only two of the five symbols are 1's and need be represented by pulses.

Another method for error detecting is that known as *parity check*. Parity refers to the quality of being equal and hence a parity check is actually an equality checking code. The coding consists of the use of an additional digit in conjunction with a given binary number. The additional digit is known as a parity digit and may be either a 0 or a 1. The parity digit is chosen to make the number of all digits in the binary group either even or odd. If the system is chosen where the digits in the binary number, plus the parity digit, are even, it is known as *even parity*. If not, the system is referred to as *odd parity*. The following indicates the addition of a parity digit to representative binary numbers:

Decimal Number	Parity Digit	Binary Number
1	1	0001
2	1	0010
3	0	0011
4	1	0100
5	0	0101

In the foregoing, it will be noted that the even parity system was employed, since the number of all the digits in the binary group (plus the parity digit) are even. For odd parity, the following would be used:

Decimal Number	Parity Digit	Binary Number
1	0	0001
2	0	0010
3	1	0011
4	0	0100
5	1	0101

In either of the foregoing cases, an error is immediately detected because the occurrence of an error changes the parity of the number. In even parity, an error is indicated by the presence of an odd parity number.

THE COUNTER

The Eccles-Jordan flip-flop circuit discussed earlier is one of the most important circuits used in digital computers. For handling binary numbers above 1, however, a group of stages must be connected together to form what is known as a *counter*. In order to understand how a counter functions, it is necessary to analyze the simple flip-flop circuit from the standpoint of the type of signals which are procured from it and the type of signals which can be utilized to actuate it. Figure 3-6 will help make this clear.

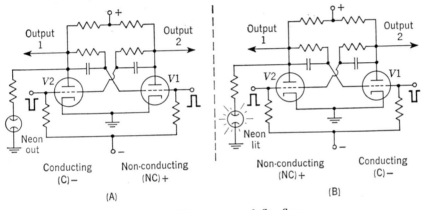

Fig. 3-6. Two states of flip-flop.

At (A) of Fig. 3-6 the flip-flop circuit is shown with the neon indicating bulb out, and hence this stage represents 0. During this time V1 is in a nonconducting state and hence the plate voltage is high because there is no voltage drop across the plate resistor. Tube V2, on the other hand, is conducting and the voltage drop across its plate resistor causes a decrease in the plus plate potential. The plus potential at the plate of V2 also appears at the grid of V1. Since the plate potential of V2, however, has decreased, it now appears at the grid of V1 sufficiently below the amplitude of the negative voltage applied to the grid. Thus, the negative voltage at the grid of V1 holds the latter at cut-off. The high plate potential at V1 is coupled to the grid of V2 and is sufficiently higher than the negative potential applied to the grid of V2 to hold the latter at conduction.

As mentioned earlier, in a bistable circuit of this type, an output can be derived from the anode of either V1 or V2 as shown. Except when the circuit is flipped over, the voltages at the anodes are steady-state conditions and do not represent a changing signal voltage.

There are two common methods which can be employed for tripping the circuit shown at (A) in order to represent the binary digit 1. One method is to apply a positive pulse to the grid of V1. Since the grid of V1 has a negative potential on it, this tube is cut off and is not conducting. The application of a positive pulse to the grid of V1 overcomes the negative cut-off potential and causes the tube to conduct. In consequence the plus potential at the anode of V1 would decrease. The decreasing positive signal, applied to the grid of V2, permits the negative voltage applied to the grid from the power supply to become dominant and cut off the tube.

A second method for tripping the circuit shown at (A) is to apply a negative pulse to the grid of V2. The negative pulse will drive the tube beyond cut-off and again the circuit flips over. When the circuit shown at (A) has been flipped over by the application of a pulse, the condition shown at (B) will prevail. Here, V1 is now in a conducting state while V2 is in a nonconducting state. When the circuit is flipped over from that shown at (A) to that shown at (B), a negative-going signal is developed at the output terminal No. 2 because the positive potential at the anode of V1 decreases. Also, when the circuit flips over, a positive-going signal appears at output No. 1, because V2 changes from a conducting state to a nonconducting state, and hence the plate voltage at the anode of V2 rises sharply.

In order to reset or flip the circuit shown at (B) back to its original state such as at (A), a negative pulse must be applied to the grid of V1, or a positive pulse to the grid of V2. In some instances one grid input is used to set the stage and the other grid input is used to reset or clear the stage. On other occasions, however, separate reset pulses are not employed, as will be shown subsequently. An understanding of the polarity of the pulses necessary at the grids, and the polarity of the signals obtainable at each ouptut, will aid in understanding how these circuits are combined to perform useful functions in digital computers.

One application of combined flip-flop stages is in the counter system of computers. A single stage flip-flop circuit can indicate only 0 or 1; hence it is necessary to utilize a number of successive stages for increasing the numbers which are to be handled. To increase the number handling capabilities of flip-flops, successive stages are connected together so that the output from one stage is applied to the input of the next stage.

Figure 3-7 shows two stages connected together. Additional stages would be interconnected in the same manner as shown for the two stages in Fig. 3-7. In this particular system, all the stages can be

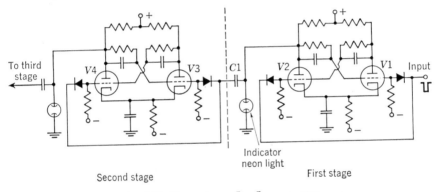

Fig. 3-7. Two stage flip-flop counter.

reset by a temporary removal of the negative voltage to the grid of the second tube in the flip-flop. Thus, the removal of the negative voltage to the grid of V2 would cause the tube to conduct and clear this stage. Clearing pulses could also be applied to the individual grids by separate input leads as shown in subsequent illustrations. For the system shown at Fig. 3-7, a single input is provided. Note that a crystal diode is at the input to the grid of V1 and another crystal diode is at the input to the grid of V2. Both grids are connected together as shown, so that an input pulse applied at V1 will also appear at the grid of V2. Negative pulses are applied to the input, each negative pulse representing a single digit.

As shown earlier at (A) of Fig. 3-6, when the input stage is cleared $V1$ is in a nonconducting state and $V2$ is in a conducting state. If a negative pulse is applied simultaneously to both grids, the negative pulse appearing at the grid of $V1$ will have no effect because this grid is already negative and the tube is cut off. A negative pulse at $V2$, however, will cause the stage to reset and hence flip over to register one. At this time, the plate potential at $V2$ rises and the neon bulb will light. The rising plate potential at $V2$ is coupled via capacitor $C1$ to the grids of the second stage flip-flop. This stage is in a zero state, and a positive pulse at the grid of $V3$ would cause it to flip over. The crystal diodes, however, prevent the positive pulse from appearing at the grids and hence the second stage is not affected by the positive signal which is developed at the plate of $V2$.

When the second negative pulse appears at the input to the first stage, it will cause $V1$ to go into cut-off and flip the stage over. The negative pulse also appears at the grid of $V2$, but since this tube is already at cut-off, it will have no effect. When this stage flips over, the voltage at $V2$ decreases and the neon bulb goes out. The decreasing voltage at $V2$ is coupled via capacitor $C1$ to the second stage grids. Since this stage is in the zero state, a negative pulse at the grid of $V4$ will cause the circuit to flip over. Tube $V4$ is then cut off and plate voltage reaches a maximum value causing the second stage neon bulb to light. Since the second stage now represents 1 and the first stage 0, the two stages now represent the binary number 10 which is equivalent to the decimal number 2. Thus, a succession of such circuits form binary counters and will store any numbers which have been entered for as long a time as voltages are applied to the circuit.

Figure 3-8 shows, in block diagram form, four such counters connected together. Thus, if seven pulses are applied to the input of the first stage, the various neon bulbs would light to indicate the *binary* number 111 (decimal 7). If four additional pulses are applied to the input, the neon bulbs would light as the various stages set and reset, to indicate the binary number 1011 (decimal 11). Thus, a number of flip-flop circuits, when strung together, will convert a train of pulses representing individual digits into their binary equivalent sum, as well as store them; and the counter will "accumulate" the binary numbers as well as adding up groups of sequential digits applied to the input. In the four stages shown in Fig. 3-8, the eleven digits which had been applied result in the

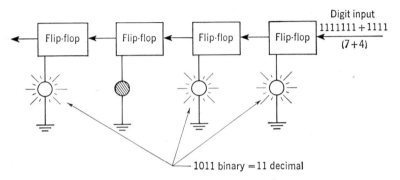

Fig. 3-8. Counter, accumulator, and storage.

three neon bulbs being lit as illustrated, representing a 1011 binary number which had been converted from the decimal equivalent 11. Four stages such as shown in Fig. 3-8 will count up to 15 (all the bulbs lit and indicating the binary number 1111). For a higher count, additional stages must be added.

In computers, neon bulbs are indicators of what is going on within the circuit and are not necessarily representative of the type of pulses (negative or positive) which are employed. In some applications, a neon indicator may be connected to the anode circuit of each tube. In such an instance, the neon bulb at the anode of the tube which triggers the next stage is referred to as a "one" neon and the neon connected to the input anode is referred to as a "zero" neon. For the purposes of this discussion, however, a clearer understanding can be had if reference is made only to a neon bulb connected to the second (trigger) anode of the flip-flop. If this neon is lit, it is an indication that the state of the flip-flop represents "1." Thus, by using the neon bulb indication as a symbol for the particular state of the flip-flop, the discussion based on such a symbol will be undstood more readily.

Capacitance coupling is utilized between the output anode of one flip-flop stage and the input circuit of the next stage in order to procure a pulse output. During a particular stable state of the flip-flop stage the plate voltage of the output anode may be of high potential, while in the other state it will be of low potential, depending on whether the tube is conducting or nonconducting. Either state represents a *steady-state* condition, and the capacitor used for coupling will pass on only the signal *change* and not the steady-state condition.

When a number of stages of flip-flops are connected together to form a counter, the neon bulb indicators bear a similarity to the wheel registry of the mechanical binary counter as will be seen by reference to Fig. 3-4. Thus, the numeral in the binary column would indicate a lighted neon bulb (or bulbs) for the decimal figures shown in the right hand column. For example, when six pulses have been inserted into the counter, the second and third neon tubes would be lit, with the first and fourth tubes being out. On the other hand, at the count of nine, the first and fourth neon bulbs would be lit, with the second and third out.

If consideration is given to the number of times a neon bulb lights up with respect to the number of pulses entered into a particular flip-flop, it would be found that a flip-flop circuit is actually a divider and for this reason is sometimes referred to as a *scaler*, since it will scale down or divide an input. If, for instance, two pulses are injected into the first stage, the neon bulb will light only once, indicating that this stage divides by 2. The addition of a second stage will cause the device to divide by 4, because for every four pulses inserted into the first stage input, only one pulse appears at the output of the second stage. The output from the third stage is only one tripping pulse for every eight tripping pulses entered into the input of the first stage, etc. Hence, the system actually is a divider as well as a binary counter. The output from the fourth stage is one pulse for every sixteen entered into the first stage, and hence the limit for binary representation of a four stage counter is 16 (scale of sixteen counter).

A series of flip-flop circuits can also be employed to represent decimal numbers (scale of ten) by making circuit changes so that a four stage system will trip to 0 at the count of ten instead of at the count of sixteen. Such a group of flip-flop circuits is known as a *decade counter* because it will count up to the decimal number

9, at which time the application of one or more pulses at the input would reset all the stages to the zero position, and at the same time produce an output pulse which would trip a fifth stage to indicate the number 10. Such a decade counter can, of course, also be used to indicate fractional units if desired. If fractional units are handled, however, it would be necessary to utilize one decade counter (four flip-flops) for each decimal place.

Figure 3-9 shows a four stage counter which is designed so that all four stages will be cleared upon the application of the tenth

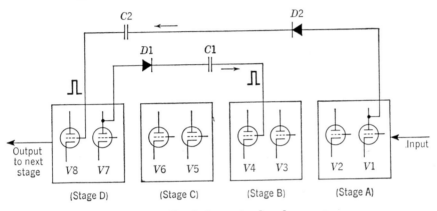

Fig. 3-9. Feedback loops in decade counter.

input pulse. For the purpose of this discussion, the four stages are labeled A, B, C, and D. Initially, each stage is at a zero state, with characteristics as indicated at (A) of Fig. 3-6, where the first tube is in a nonconducting state and the second is in a conducting state.

Use of the chart shown in Fig. 3-10 in conjunction with Figs. 3-6 and 3-9 will help indicate how the decade counter functions. The chart in Fig. 3-10 shows the various "conducting" states of the tubes represented by a C and the "nonconducting" states indicated by NC. At the count of nine, the characteristics of the tubes are as shown in Fig. 3-10, opposite the decimal value of 9 on the chart. It is at this particular time that the circuit must be ready for resetting to 0 when another pulse comes in. Since stages A and D are in the "on" state, they must be converted to 0 upon the arrival of the next input pulse to the first stage. The tenth pulse would normally reset stage A to 0 so this presents no problem. When stage

A resets to 0, however, it applies a pulse to stage B and turns the latter on. Hence, provisions must be made to prevent stage B from going on, and at the same time resetting stage D to 0 so that it will

Decimal Value	Stage D		Stage C		Stage B		Stage A		Decimal Value
	V8	V7	V6	V5	V4	V3	V2	V1	
0	C—	+NC	C—	+NC	C—	+NC	C—	+NC	0
1	C—	+NC	C—	+NC	C—	+NC	NC+	—C	1
2	C—	+NC	C—	+NC	NC+	—C	C—	+NC	2
3	C—	+NC	C—	+NC	NC+	—C	NC+	—C	3
4	C—	+NC	NC+	—C	C—	+NC	C—	+NC	4
5	C—	+NC	NC+	—C	C—	+NC	NC+	—C	5
6	C—	+NC	NC+	—C	NC+	—C	C—	+NC	6
7	C—	+NC	NC+	—C	NC+	—C	NC+	—C	7
8	NC+	—C	C—	+NC	C—	+NC	C—	+NC	8
9	NC+	—C	C—	+NC	C—	+NC	NC+	—C	9

Note: Minus sign indicates a decrease in plate potential; a plus sign indicates an increase. A plus sign at V2, V4, V6, and V8 denotes a lighted neon tube.

Fig. 3-10. Tube characteristics for a decade counter.

send a triggering pulse on the tenth count to the fifth stage. This can be done by use of any of several feedback processes, one of which is shown in Fig. 3-9. One feedback loop is attached from the anode of V1 to the grid of V8, and the other feedback loop is attached to the anode of V7 and is applied to the grid of V4.

The feedback loops are put into operation when the tenth pulse arrives at the input of V1. Referring to the chart in Fig. 3-10, it will be seen that at count nine an input pulse causes the plate of V2 to go into conduction and develop a negative pulse which is sent to the next stage. In the meantime, V1 goes from a conducting to a nonconducting state, and a rising positive potential is developed. This rising positive voltage is fed to the grid of V8 through diode D2, and capacitor C2, and causes stage D to flip over. Thus, stage D flips to its zero status, and the plate of V7, which had a low amplitude voltage, now rises (positive direction) to a high voltage. The positive voltage rise developed at the anode of V7 is fed back to the grid of V4 at the same time that a negative pulse arrives from stage A. The positive feedback pulse from V7, however, overrides the effect which the negative input pulse to stage B would have, and hence the feedback pulse holds stage B in its zero position. Thus, all stages flip to zero position, and as stage D flips to its zero position, one output pulse is obtained for tripping the next decade counter.

The positive voltages developed at the anode of V1 during the second, fourth, and sixth counts are ineffective in tripping V8 because the latter is in a conducting state at these times and would require a negative pulse for tripping. The negative pulses developed at V1 are blocked by diode 2 in series with the feedback line. At count eight, the positive voltage developed at V1 is ineffective because, at that instant, stage D has not yet flipped over, and does not do so until stages B and C have flipped over, by which time the voltage at V1 plate will have become a steady-state condition which is blocked by C2. Capacitor C1 prevents the steady-state direct current of V7 from being applied to the grid of V4 during the initial 7 counts, when V7 is nonconducting. At count eight, tube V7 is changed to conduction, and plate potential decreases. The negative-direction change, however, is not instrumental in affecting V4, since the diode in series with the feedback line conducts only for a positive pulse. The diodes must have a high forward-to-back ratio of resistance, to prevent the transfer of a negative voltage from V1 plate to V8 grid, or V7 plate to V4 grid.

Other feedback loops can also be used. For instance, the V1 to V8 loop can be replaced with a V2 (anode) to V7 (grid) loop, feeding a negative pulse to stage D to trip at the tenth count.

Decade counters are, of course, particularly suitable for the binary coded decimal system discussed earlier. Reference to Fig. 3-5 will indicate the manner of usage. In this figure, let each of the four vertical lights represent one flip-flop stage of a decade counter. The last stage of the first counter (top flip-flop of first vertical counter) feeds the first flip-flop stage of the second decade counter (bottom flip-flop of second vertical counter). The output from the second decade counter (top flip-flop of second vertical section) is applied to the input of the third decade counter, etc. Thus, instead of representing all the flip-flops of the successive decade counters on a single horizontal plane, the groupings shown in Fig. 3-5 will indicate the binary counts vertically and the decimal counts horizontally as explained in the text accompanying Fig. 3-5.

The binary counters are devices which take a serial train of units and convert them to an electronically stored representation as previously mentioned. Thus, if five pulses are injected into a binary counter, the binary counter will register 101 and thus has converted a train of five pulses into a binary count. The binary counter is additive in its characteristics; that is, it can accumulate counts, since another train of serial pulses can be inserted and the binary sum of the first and second entries will be produced in the counter. For instance, if five pulses had been inserted initially as aforementioned, the counter would register 101 which is the binary equivalent of five. If three more pulses are inserted, the counter would register 1000, which is the binary equivalent of 8. The binary and decade counters not only convert the serial pulse train to a binary number, but will add successive trains to the amount registered in the counters.

From the foregoing, the term *accumulator* could be applied to the binary counter since the latter will accumulate the sums of the numbers serially injected into the input. Actually, however, the word accumulator should be applied only to the type of flip-flop counters which will accept a *binary* number in serial or parallel form and add such a number to the binary number already stored, as more fully detailed later.

Counters are also formed by using flip-flop stages in cascade, and feeding the output from the last flip-flop of the group to the input of the first flip-flop as shown at (A) of Fig. 3-11. This forms a closed loop or "ring" and hence this device is known as a *ring counter.*

At (B) of Fig. 3-11 is a partial schematic of the flip-flop circuit No. 1 indicating the two input lines to the grid circuits. The input from the previous stage is applied to both crystal diodes $D1$ and $D2$, thus permitting negative pulses to be applied to the grids of $V1$ and $V2$. This is similar to the method employed in the two stage counter previously shown in Fig. 3-7. Another pulse input is provided by the reset line which permits a negative pulse to be applied to $V1$ only. Diode $D1$ prevents the negative reset pulse from appearing at the plate circuit of the previous stage, and also prevents the negative reset pulse from appearing at the grid of V2. This diode (D1) also prevents a positive pulse from the previous stage from triggering at the time when the previous stage is triggered into an "on" position.

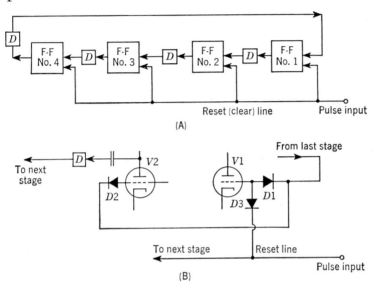

Fig. 3-11. Ring counter.

In the ring counter only one flip-flop is in the "on" triggered state. For the purposes of this discussion, assume flip-flop No. 1 has been tripped, indicating the entry of a single pulse representing a single digit. Subsequent pulses are entered into the circuit via the reset or "clear" line as shown, and hence the input pulses are applied simultaneously to all the flip-flop circuits.

When a pulse is entered into the reset line, it will not affect those stages which are in the "off" position; hence if only flip-flop No. 1 in Fig. 3-11 is "on" it will be the only one which is cleared. When this occurs, the output pulse will trigger the second flip-flop to represent an "on" condition. Thus, in this ring counter, when the second flip-flop is "on" it represents the number 2 and holds this in storage for as long as electrical power is applied to the ring.

Between each stage is a delay line, the purpose of which is to delay the triggering of one flip-flop circuit by the preceding one at the time the clearing pulses are present. Without the delay the result, in the example just given, would be that the first stage would try to trigger the second stage at the time the clearing pulse is entered. The delay line holds back the triggering pulse until the reset pulse is no longer present. In some circuitry, the flipping over may be sufficiently slow to permit elimination of the delay lines.

As successive pulses are applied to the input line, the "on" state moves progressively from one flip-flop stage to another and, when the final stage is cleared, it triggers No. 1 stage and the cycle starts over. Ring counters may have as many stages as are desired and are not limited to four as shown in Fig. 3-11. Also, the feedback loop can be dispensed with if some other means is employed for triggering the first flip-flop circuit.

Another form of the ring counter, as shown in Fig. 3-12, dispenses with the delay lines by using an extra input flip-flop circuit

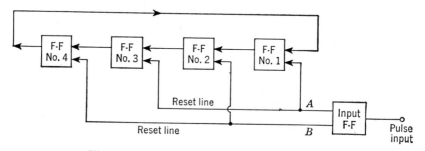

Fig. 3-12. Ring counter without delay lines.

as shown. The flip-flop circuits are hooked up in cascade, as in the two stage counter illustrated in Fig. 3-7. In this ring counter an additional flip-flop stage is used, and designated "input FF" in Fig. 3-12. The latter stage has two output circuits marked A and B, each coming from one of the anode circuits of the input flip-flop. Each output line is applied to alternate flip-flop stages as shown. The output line A, for instance, is applied to the reset line of the odd numbered flip-flop stages, while the output marked B is applied to the even numbered flip-flop stages. As with the previously discussed ring counter, a number of stages may be employed, depending on the requirements of the computer.

The reset line inputs plus the input circuits from previous stages are similar to that shown at (B) of Fig. 3-11, with the diodes permitting only negative pulses to be applied to the grids. The reset line applies a negative pulse to the grids of the first tube of each stage only. An inspection of the partial drawing at (B) of Fig. 3-11 will indicate that a negative pulse applied via $D3$ is blocked from the grid of $V2$ because of the reversion resistance characteristics of diode $D1$.

As with the previously discussed ring counter, only one flip-flop stage is in the "on" position at any time. Assume that for Fig. 3-12 the flip-flop stage No. 2 is in the "on" position. When a pulse is applied to the input flip-flop, a positive pulse is produced at the A output and a negative pulse at the B output. The positive pulse at the A output is blocked by the reset line grid diodes and hence has no effect. The negative pulse at line B will clear the flip-flop stage No. 2, and in doing so the latter stage sends a negative pulse to the third flip-flop stage and triggers it to the "on" position. The negative pulse on line B which also arrives at the input to the fourth flip-flop will have no effect, since the latter stage is in the "off" position.

When another pulse is applied to the input flip-flop, a negative pulse is present at the output line A and a positive pulse at output line B. Again, the positive pulse on the output line B (applied to the even numbered flip-flops) is blocked by the grid diodes. The negative pulse on line A, however, trips the third flip-flop, clearing it and at the same time producing an output pulse from the third flip-flop which triggers the fourth. Again, the negative pulse from line A will not affect the first flip-flop, because the latter is already in the "off" position and hence cannot be cleared or reset. Thus, successive pulses applied to the input flip-flop will move the "on" indication along the various flip-flop stages progressively. When the last stage is cleared, the loop triggers the first flip-flop and thus completes the ring.

As previously mentioned, a free-running multivibrator synchronized by a crystal oscillator is usually employed as the source of the pulses used in a computer. Such a multivibrator is often used to drive a multistage ring counter, as shown in Fig. 3-13. Output pulses can then be procured from the various ring counters to represent various time relationships. Such pulses are switched as required to any of the gating or calculating circuits described later. The ring counter, in conjunction with the multivibrator, is often referred to as the "clock" because it times both the original pulses and their distribution throughout the ring counter.

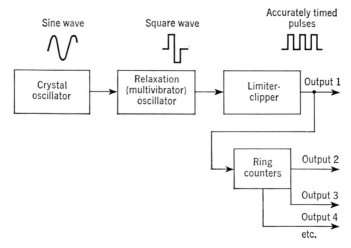

Fig. 3-13. Generation and frequency control of pulses.

COUNT DETECTION

A particular number in a counter can be obtained from the latter (read out) in its binary form and applied to other calculating circuits or to storage devices. There are occasions, however, when it is necessary to have an indication of a particular number in a counter, such indication being other than binary. The indication may be in the form of a voltage which appears only when a certain number is present, so that this voltage can be applied to another circuit to perform a particular function such as indicating the number by lighting up a display number, or tripping some relay or gating circuit. The indicator can also be in the form of a zero voltage when a certain number is to be indicated, and the presence of a voltage if the number to be read is absent. Thus, a relay or an electronic gate such as described later can be held open by a voltage, and closed when the required number eliminates the voltage.

An indication of the presence of a specific number can be obtained from a counter by use of a diode switch arrangement such as shown in Fig. 3-14. Here, three flip-flop stages are shown, though of course as many as desired can be employed. In a flip-flop circuit, the anode of the output tube has a negative potential when the flip-flop is in a zero state, and a positive potential when it is in the

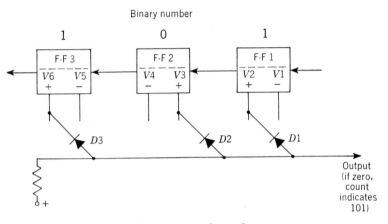

Fig. 3-14. Diode network to detect counts.

"one" or "on" state, as previously mentioned. Hence, the diodes can be connected to the proper plates to give an indication when a certain number is in the counter. For instance, if the binary number 101 (5) has been stored in the flip-flops as shown in Fig. 3-14, the first diode (D1) would be connected so that a plus voltage from the flip-flop is applied to D1. Diodes D2 and D3 would be connected to successive flip-flops in the same manner. When this is the case, none of the diodes would conduct because of their reverse-voltage hookup, and hence the output would be zero if the counter indicates the binary number 101. For any other number, however, a negative voltage would be present at one or more of the diodes, and the diodes would conduct, causing a negative voltage to appear at the output. For instance, if the binary number 100 were in the counter, the first flip-flop would be in the "off" state and hence V1 would be positive and V2 negative. The negative voltage applied to the diode D1 would appear at the output. Only when the individual flip-flops are in the states shown, would the output be zero to indicate the count of 101. A plus voltage applied to the diode line provides a return circuit to the power source, and when none of the diodes is conducting the output reference level is considered to be zero.

A group of diode networks is used to detect counts in progressively higher order as shown in Fig. 3-15. The output from the first diode line (horizontal) will detect a zero count, the output

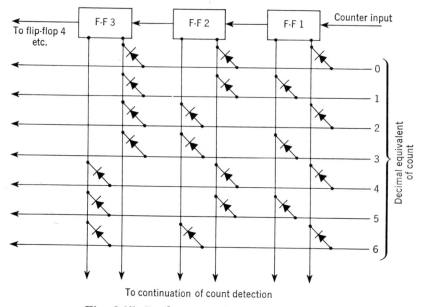

Fig. 3-15. Diode matrix for detecting counts.

from the second horizontal diode line will detect a one count, and so forth. Note that the output lines from the various flip-flops are shown in a vertical plane, and the output from each diode network consists of the horizontal lines, each of which represents a specific number. An arrangement such as this is known as a *diode matrix*. (For additional information with respect to the use of the matrix layout, see Chapter 7.)

The reference level for each horizontal line can be set at —25 or —30 volts to indicate no detection of the specific number, and zero (or plus) voltage to indicate the presence of the particular number assigned to that line.

Questions Relating to Chapter 3

1. *a*) Using the table in the text indicating the powers of 2, write the binary numbers which represent 13, 26, 32, and 47.

b) What numbers do the binary figures 111, 1011, and 1111 represent in base ten numbers?

2. Briefly define the following terms: addend; augend; minuend; subtrahend; multiplicand.

3. What is the binary sum which results from the addition of binary numbers 101 plus 1101? What is the base ten equivalent of the binary sum?

4. *a*) Convert 11 and 22 to binary numbers and add them together. What is the binary sum?
   b) What is the binary number which results when 7 is subtracted from 21?

5. *a*) What is the binary number which results when 101 binary is subtracted from 1111 binary, and the result added to the binary number 111?
   b) What is the binary product when the binary number 111 is multiplied by 101?
   c) Convert the numbers 7 and 8 to binary numbers and multiply one by the other. What is the binary product?

6. What is meant by the binary-coded decimal system? Express 248 in this system.

7. *a*) Express the numbers 18, 20, and 32 in excess-three code.
   b) Explain what is meant by the Gray code.

8. Explain what is meant by floating decimal point notation. Express 13,894 in this notation.

9. Draw a three stage flip-flop system, and indicate which tubes are conducting and which are nonconducting when the binary number 101 has been stored.

10. *a*) What is meant by a decade counter?
    b) Compare the function of a decade counter to that of a binary counter.

11. Show by block diagram a counter and indicate which bulbs would be lit if three pulses are inserted initially and then three more pulses are inserted at a later time.

12. Explain briefly how a ring counter operates.

13. Explain by what means a specific number can be read out of a counter to give an indication of the count.

4

□ □ □
■ □ □
□ □ □

Special Circuits

INTRODUCTION

The basic flip-flop type of binary counter previously described converts a serial train of digits into an equivalent binary sum, and will add or "accumulate" successive entries. In modified form it will also perform other tasks, as more fully detailed later. The flip-flop circuit alone, however, is unable to perform all the tasks called for in a modern computer, because the latter must be able to perform the functions of addition, subtraction, multiplication, and division, using inputs composed of both serial train binary numbers as well as binary numbers in parallel form. To perform such diversified tasks requires the use of other circuits in addition to the basic flip-flop circuit. Such additional circuits consist of switching and gating circuits, delay lines, as well as special circuits which are of a selective nature. These various circuits are necessary to complete the processes involved in calculations where input numbers are of binary form. By combining these special circuits, the various and special processes involved in calculations (such as "borrowing" and "carrying") are performed electronically and at high speeds.

Besides the delay and switching circuits mentioned above, a few special circuits are also employed which are in the form of "logical gates" in the sense that they are discriminatory in nature and will provide an output only under specific input conditions.

These special gating circuits are based on the logical concepts of a special algebra called "Boolean" algebra, named after George Boole (1815–1864), the British mathematician and logician who originated the system. Boolean algebra relates the laws of mathematics with logic and the binary notation used in digital computers stems from this logic-math system. Boole's system of algebra concerns operations and ideas of logic which are particularly applicable to circuit behavior where "on" and "off" circuit conditions are involved.

George Boole, of course, had no idea regarding the extent to which his logical reasoning precepts would be utilized eventually in computer design. His algebra, however, has grown by additions and modifications by later mathematicians, until it is now a valuable tool for designing various computer circuits or other branches of cybernetics wherein logical design is applied to electromechanical devices.

In Boolean algebra, addition takes on the logical representation of "or," and hence is adaptable to systems where one or the other result must be obtained. Multiplication takes on the characteristics of "and." Boolean precepts were first utilized in switching systems of telephones and are a valuable tool in the design of computer devices. For those contemplating advanced design practices, reference should be made to the bibliography in the appendix, wherein books giving extended treatment of the subject are listed.

For one unfamiliar with computer terminology, the special logical circuits used have strange sounding names such as *and-gates, or-gates*, and *inhibitors*. Sometimes they are simply called *and*-circuits, *or*-circuits, etc. Actually, however, they perform the functions relative to *and* and *or* conditions, and are extremely useful in making up ingenious electronic circuit combinations which perform multiplication, division, and other related mathematical processes.

The reader is already familiar with some of these "logical" circuits used in ordinary walks of life. A door bell, for instance, which can be rung from either the front door or the back door employs an *or*-circuit, because either the push button on the front door *OR* the push button on the back door rings the bell, *or* both buttons (if pushed simultaneously) will cause the bell to ring. An *and*-circuit is employed in burglar-alarm systems. Suppose a switch were placed in the door of the dwelling to ring an alarm, but a master switch were also employed to open the circuit and prevent the ringing of the alarm when the owner is home. Thus, the alarm will not ring if either switch is open, but it will ring *only* if the door switch *AND* the master switch are both closing the circuit.

The electronic logical-gate circuits employed in computers are, of course, not the simple switching devices mentioned above for illustration purposes, though they perform similar functions. In this chapter various special circuits of this type are discussed, and the method in which they are combined to form multipliers, adders, etc. are detailed in the next chapter.

AND-CIRCUIT

And-circuits can be designed around crystal diodes, vacuum tubes, or transistors. A basic and-circuit using crystal diodes is shown at (A) of Fig. 4-1. This circuit uses to advantage the high reverse resistance characteristics of the diode in one direction, and the low forward resistance in the other direction.

In practical circuitry, design is directly related to the nature of the signals employed. In some applications a negative signal is considered 0, and a positive signal represents the digit 1. In other instances, the absence of a signal or pulse may represent 0, while the presence of a pulse represents 1. For the circuit shown in Fig. 4-1, a negative potential is representative of 0, and a positive potential indicates the digit 1.

At (B) is shown the and-circuit under conditions of no signal input. Here, a negative potential is applied to the diode $D1$ and another negative potential is also applied to the diode $D2$. In such an instance, both diodes will conduct because of their low forward resistance. Current flows from the minus voltage source through the diodes in parallel and up through the load resistor (R_L). Because of the low forward resistance of the two diodes, virtually all of the voltage drop will occur across the load resistance. Under this condition the output signal is of a negative potential and hence rep-resents 0. At (C) is shown the condition where a positive pulse is applied at input No. 1. The positive pulse overcomes the negative

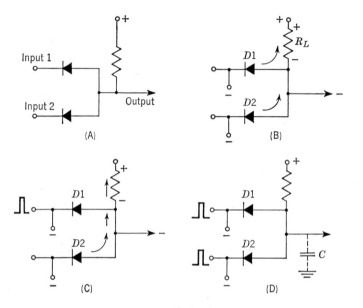

Fig. 4-1. Diode and-circuit.

potential applied to diode $D1$, and the latter conducts very little because of the high reverse resistance. The output, however, is still effectively connected to the negative potential at the input through the low forward resistance of diode $D2$. Hence, the output is still a negative potential. At (D), the circuit is shown with a positive pulse applied at the first input and another positive pulse applied at the second input. Now neither diode conducts any appreciable current, and hence there will be virtually no voltage drop across the load resistance because of the absence of current flow. (Actually, some little current flows because the crystal diodes are not perfect diodes in the sense that they do not conduct in one direction and conduct in the other direction. In their so-called noncon-ducting state crystal diodes have a high resistance, but a little cur-rent still flows. For the purposes of circuit analysis, however, it can be assumed that a perfect diode is in usage.) With both diodes presenting a high reverse resistance, the output from the and-circuit will be a plus potential to represent the digit 1.

The capacitor C shown in the dotted connections at the output represents the input capacitance of the following circuit, as well as stray wiring capacitances and the inherent capacitance of the diodes. The shunting effect of the capacitor integrates to a slight extent the output pulse waveform and modifies somewhat the leading edge. Stray capacitances and other circuit capacitances of this type are a factor in limiting the usefulness of the circuit, and must be taken into consideration in design work.

From the foregoing, it is evident the and-circuit develops no output unless a pulse is applied at input No. 1 at the same time that a pulse is applied to input No. 2. Both pulses must occur simultaneously. Because both pulses must coincide, the circuit is sometimes referred to as a *coincidence circuit*. Hence, the and-circuit function may be shown as follows:

INPUT		OUTPUT
No. 1	No. 2	
Pulse	Zero	Zero
Zero	Pulse	Zero
Pulse	Pulse	Pulse

An and-circuit using a pentode vacuum tube is shown in Fig. 4-2. The tube is a sharp cut-off type. Here, one input is applied to

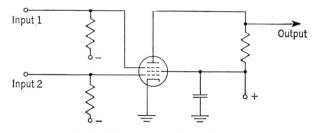

Fig. 4-2. Vacuum tube and-circuit.

the suppressor grid and the other input to the control grid. Both these grids have applied to them a negative potential of sufficient amplitude to cut off the tube. Since either grid, when biased to cut-off, is capable of preventing tube conduction, current will flow in the anode circuit only when both grids have a positive potential applied to them simultaneously, such positive potential having sufficient amplitude to overcome the cut-off bias. Thus, if a positive pulse is applied to the input No. 1, but no pulse is applied to input No. 2, the negative potential at the latter is sufficient to hold the tube at cut-off. Similarly, an input at No. 2 but none at No. 1 will still be insufficient to cause the tube to conduct. When a positive signal is applied at input No. 1 at the same time that a positive signal is applied to input No. 2, the tube will conduct and a negative pulse appears at the output. This is then suitable for application to circuits where a negative pulse represents the digit 1 or for other applications where a negative pulse is required. If a positive pulse is needed, the output from the pentode and-circuit would have to be applied to a pulse amplifier which would invert the phase of the signal and provide a positive pulse output. A resistor can also be placed between cathode and ground and the output signal obtained from across the resistor. In such an instance the circuit becomes a cathode follower type and-circuit with a positive polarity output pulse.

A typical transistor and-circuit is shown in Fig. 4-3 and utilizes

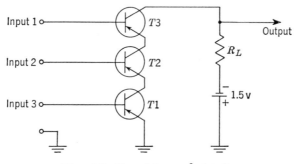

Fig. 4-3. Transistor and-circuit.

three surface barrier transistors in a cascode hookup. The word *cascode* stems from the definition of a similar hookup utilized with vacuum tube circuits, where the output from the anode of a vacuum tube amplifier is applied to the cathode of the following stage. The term is used to differentiate between the hookup known as *cascade*, wherein the output from the anode of one tube is applied to the grid of the next tube. With the cascode transistor circuit shown in Fig. 4-3, the emitter of one transistor is directly coupled to the collector of the succeeding transistor and hence the designation *cascode*.

The and-circuit shown operates because of the ability of the surface barrier transistor to function when the collector potential is much lower than the base potential in a common-emitter circuit. Hence, the current through the common load resistor is controlled by the three input circuits, one for each base as shown. If the power supply input voltage had any one of the base inputs brought to a value sufficiently positive to be near the positive ground potential, the particular transistor at which a pulse is applied to the base is cut off, and the series path through the three transistors is therefore opened. When the path is open, the output voltage is approximately 1.5 volts minus, unless a pulse is applied to each input simultaneously. In order to procure an output, all three inputs must be driven sufficiently negative simultaneously so that a low impedance path for the current is provided through the transistors. The current path through the transistors, and through the load resistor, R_L, will produce an output across the latter. With the gate open and current flowing through the series path and the resistor, the output voltage drops to approximately 0.1 volt minus with respect to ground, representing an 1.4 voltage differential. The increase in the amount of current through the load resistor thus produces a less negative potential at the output and this represents a rising positive voltage. Thus, when all three input signals are present simultaneously, a positive output pulse is secured.

The and-circuit has many uses in digital computers because of its gating characteristics. There are many occasions when pulses must either be gated into other circuits or gated out. As previously described, pulses can be applied to both inputs of the and-circuit to produce an output. When this is done, one set of pulses can be considered to be gating in the other set and producing an output. It is possible, however, to gate pulses through an and-circuit by using a steady-state voltage at the second input. This is shown in Fig. 4-4. At (A), a partial diagram of a flip-flop circuit is shown, where the flip-flop is in an "off" state with V1 not conducting and V2 conducting. When V2 is in a conducting state, a large voltage drop occurs across the load resistor and the anode voltage is negative as

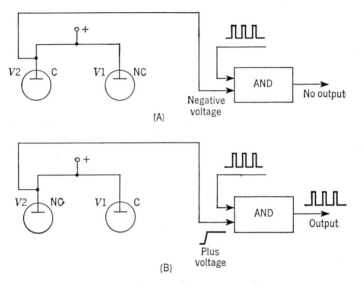

(A)

(B)

Fig. 4-4. Flip-flop used to gate and-circuit.

previously described. This negative voltage, applied to the second input of the and-gate, acts to gate out any pulses which are applied to the first input line, because the signals appearing at the two input lines must coincide in polarity. If the flip-flop circuit is triggered so that it is in an "on" state as shown at (B) of Fig. 4-4, V2 will be nonconducting and hence the anode will be positive. When this steady-state plus voltage is applied to the second input of an and-circuit, it will open the and-gate and permit the entry of all signals appearing at the first input terminal. Thus, if a series of pulses are appearing at the first input terminal (or a binary number) it will appear at the output of the and-circuit.

Note that the and-circuit which is gated by a flip-flop resembles in function somewhat that of the start-stop multivibrator previously discussed. The output from the start-stop multivibrator can also be used as a trigger for changing the status of the and-circuit. With the start-stop multivibrator, the application of a pulse generates a positive pulse output waveform; the application of a second pulse to the multivibrator stops the positive waveform signal. With the flip-flop, the positive steady-state voltage is also produced by triggering the flip-flop, and the negative voltage for closing the and-gate is produced by applying a second triggering pulse.

The diode matrix count indicators illustrated earlier in Figs. 3-14 and 3-15 also exemplify the and-gate principle, by not indicating a certain count until *all* diodes are supplied a plus potential.

OR-CIRCUIT

An or-circuit is one which has two or more inputs and will provide an output signal if a signal is applied to any or all of the inputs. A typical two input or-circuit using crystal diodes is shown in Fig. 4-5. This circuit will produce an output when a pulse is applied to input No. 1, input No. 2, or both. An inspection of Fig. 4-5 will

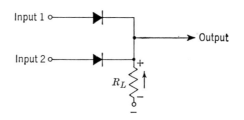

Fig. 4-5. Diode or-circuit.

show the similarity between this circuit and the and-circuit previously discussed. The or-circuit is similar to the and-circuit except for the reversal of the diode connections and the application of a negative potential to the load resistor.

With both diodes conducting, current flow through the load resistor is in the direction shown by the arrow and would represent a steady-state condition in the absence of an input signal. Upon the application of a positive polarity signal at input No. 1, the diode connected to this input would have increased conduction and the voltage across the load resistor would rise, producing a positive signal output. Similarly, a signal applied at input No. 2 will cause a rise in the voltage drop across the load resistor, as would the application of signals simultaneously to both input No. 1 and input No. 2. Hence, the or-circuit function may be shown as follows:

INPUT		OUTPUT
No. 1	No. 2	
Pulse	Zero	Pulse
Zero	Pulse	Pulse
Pulse	Pulse	Pulse

A vacuum tube or-circuit appears in Fig. 4-6, and utilizes a dual triode as shown. A plus voltage is applied to the cathode resistor *R*3 so that the tube is biased slightly beyond the cut-off point. (By

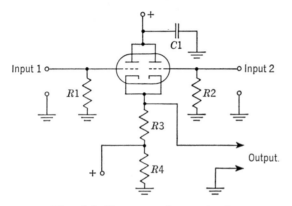

Fig. 4-6. Vacuum tube or-circuit.

making the cathode positive, the grids become relatively negative.) The output is derived from across cathode resistor combination *R*3 and *R*4, in cathode follower fashion. Because the output is not derived from the anode circuit, and the latter is by-passed by capacitor *C*1 which places the anode at *signal* ground. (Capacitor *C*1 could be the power supply filter capacitor.) As with the previous or-circuit, this or-circuit will have an output if a pulse is applied at input No. 1, at input No. 2, *or* at both inputs at the same time.

If the transistors of the and-circuit shown in Fig. 4-3 are connected in parallel instead of in cascode series, an or-circuit is produced as shown at (A) of Fig. 4-7. This is a three input or-circuit. As with the and-circuit previously discussed, two inputs could be employed as shown at (B), or more than three can be utilized. In the three input or-circuit shown at (A) of Fig. 4-7, each transistor must be made to draw enough current through the load resistor so that the output voltage decreases close to the positive ground potential. Hence, an input pulse applied at either No. 1, 2, or 3, or any combination of the three, will produce a positive pulse across the load resistor output.

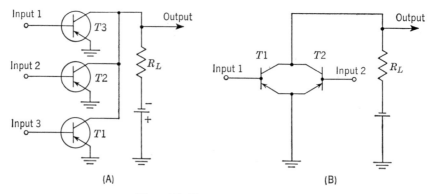

Fig. 4-7. Transistor or-circuit.

The foregoing example of the usage of transistors in an or-circuit, and the previous transistor and-circuit, indicates the simplicity which can be realized in this kind of transistor circuitry. For either the and-circuit or the or-circuit, only a single resistor is necessary and no coupling capacitors are used. Hence, either of these circuits can be constructed on a chassis having extremely small dimensions as compared with a similar or-circuit and similar and-circuit utilizing vacuum tubes and the associated components necessary for operation of the latter.

INHIBITOR CIRCUIT

An inhibitor circuit is one having two or more inputs, plus an inhibitory input. There will be an output for any input pulses except when a pulse is present at the inhibitory input. When the latter occurs, there is no output. A typical inhibitor circuit is shown in Fig. 4-8, which utilizes the and-circuit previously illustrated in Fig. 4-2 in conjunction with a phase inverting circuit. The phase inverting circuit is usually referred to as a *not*-circuit. The not-circuit is for the purpose of inverting a pulse which is applied to the input so that the output would be of opposite polarity. Thus, a not-circuit will provide a negative output pulse upon the application of positive input pulse, or vice versa. For the inhibitor circuit shown in Fig. 4-8, the suppressor grid is connected to the not-circuit via

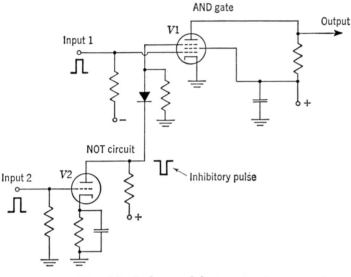

Fig. 4-8. And-not inhibiting circuit.

a diode. The purpose of the diode is to prevent the plus potential of V2 from being impressed on the suppressor grid. The suppressor grid is at cathode potential while the control grid is biased at cut-off. Thus, there will be no output from the inhibitor circuit unless a pulse is applied to input No. 1. Upon the arrival of a plus signal at the control grid, the plus potential overcomes the negative cut-off bias and the tube can then conduct and produce an output pulse. If, on the other hand, a pulse is applied to input No. 2 in the absence of a signal at input No. 1, there will be no output because the inhibitory pulse simply drives the suppressor grid into the cut-off region and the tube is already held at cut-off by the bias on the control grid. Also, if pulses are applied simultaneously to inputs No. 1 and No. 2 there will be no output, because even though the positive pulse at input No. 1 would overcome the cut-off bias at the control grid, the inhibitory pulse which arrives at the suppressor grid will drive the latter into the cut-off region and thus prevent tube conduction.

From the foregoing it is evident that the pulse input at the not-circuit will inhibit or suppress any output when a pulse is applied at input No. 1. Hence, the function of the inhibitor circuit is as follows:

INPUT		OUTPUT
No. 1	No. 2	
Pulse	Zero	Pulse
Zero	Pulse	Zero
Pulse	Pulse	Zero

The inhibitory pulse is sometimes referred to as a suppressor pulse or a prohibiting pulse.

An inhibitor circuit can also be formed without the use of an and-circuit as shown in Fig. 4-9. Here, a transformer is used to

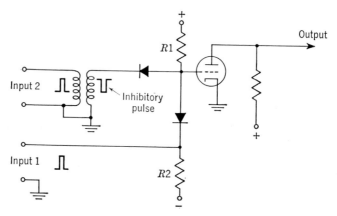

Fig. 4-9. Inhibitor circuit.

provide the proper phase inversion for the production of an inhibitory pulse. A positive potential is applied to the control grid via resistor $R1$, and a negative potential is applied to the control grid via resistor $R2$. These two opposing potentials are of such amplitude that normally a negative potential exists at the control grid, such potential having sufficient amplitude to provide cut-off bias and thus prevent tube conduction. Upon the arrival of a positive *pulse* at input No. 1, the positive potential overcomes the negative potential supplied through resistor $R2$; the positive potential supplied via $R1$ predominates at the control grid, hence the tube can now conduct and provide an output pulse. If a pulse is also applied to input No. 2 at the same time that a pulse is applied to input No. 1, there will be no output, because the negative polarity inhibitory pulse which arrives at the control grid is sufficient to drive the tube into the cut-off region. The diodes serve the purpose of preventing interaction between the plus and minus voltages.

A transistor inhibitory circuit is shown in Fig. 4-10, using an N-P-N junction transistor, in a grounded emitter circuit. Note, how-

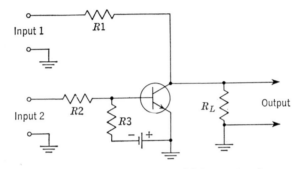

Fig. 4-10. Transistor inhibitory circuit.

ever, that the battery polarity between emitter and base is the reverse of what it would normally be in a transistor amplifier. Because of the reversed battery polarity, the transistor is cut off, and for a positive pulse applied across input No. 1 there would be a corresponding output across the load resistor (R_L). If, however, a positive pulse appears at input No. 2 at the same time that a pulse appears at input No. 1, the positive pulse input at No. 2 would overcome the battery potential and cause the transistor to operate at saturation. At saturation the transistor has a low resistance characteristic, hence effectively shorts the pulse applied at input No. 1 to ground, and thus inhibits the appearance of a pulse across the load resistor. For proper operation, the positive pulse applied across input No. 2 must be sufficiently higher in amplitude than the battery potential to overcome the latter, and to apply a high enough positive potential at base-emitter for saturation. A P-N-P junction transistor could also be employed, but with the latter the bat-

tery polarity shown in Fig. 4-10 would have to be reversed, and the
input pulses would have to be negative in polarity.

SYMBOLS

Because computer systems utilize many combinations of and-
circuits, or-circuits, etc., it is the usual practice to employ symbols
for such circuits so that a more compact schematic drawing can be
made of a portion of the computer in service manuals, operating
instructions, textbooks, etc. This procedure is similar to the use of
block diagrams for the explanations of the over-all function of radio
or television receivers once the basic circuits have been studied and
understood. In computer schematics, two types of symbol designations are employed. One method is the use of semicircular symbols
such as shown in Fig. 4-11. This symbol designation was developed

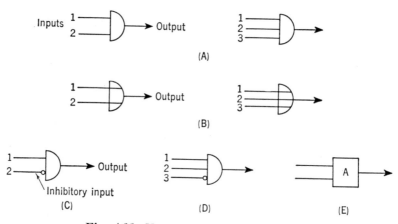

Fig. 4-11. Various gating-circuit symbols.

during the preliminary period of computer design by the engineers
concerned with the development of the SEAC digital computer of
the National Bureau of Standards. Such symbols have been used
to some extent by commercial manufacturers and familiarization
with the symbols represented in Fig. 4-11 will be of help when similar types are encountered in the field.

At (A) of Fig. 4-11, two and-gate symbols are shown. The first
one has two inputs, and the second has three inputs. And-circuits

with more than three inputs may also be encountered on occasion. As with the and-circuits previously discussed, pulses must appear at all inputs simultaneously in order to obtain an output.

At (B) of Fig. 4-11 are shown two or-circuits. These are distinguished from the and-circuits because the input lines are drawn through the semicircle as shown. As with the previously discussed or-gates, an output pulse will appear for an input pulse at either of the inputs, and an output pulse will also appear for any combination of simultaneous pulses at the inputs.

At (C) of Fig. 4-11 is shown an inhibitor circuit. An ouput will be obtained whenever a pulse is applied to input No. 1 if no pulse is applied to input No. 2. Input No. 2 is the inhibitory input and is designated by a small circle at the end of the second input line. When a pulse appears at input No. 2 it inhibits or suppresses a pulse applied to input No. 1 and prevents its entry into the circuit.

At (D) is shown an and-gate with an inhibitor. Pulses applied at inputs No. 1 and No. 2 will provide an output pulse. No output pulse will appear, however, if only a single input is applied to No. 1 or a single pulse applied to No. 2 input. If pulses are applied simultaneously to all three inputs, the pulse at input No. 3 will inhibit or suppress the pulses applied simultaneously to inputs No. 1 and 2.

In many commercial schematics, however, the semicircular symbols are not used and instead the rectangular form of symbol such as shown at (E) of Fig. 4-11 is employed. Designation of the particular circuit is made by an A for an and-circuit, an O for an or-circuit, an I for an inverter (not-) circuit, and a D for a delay line.

PULSE-BURST GENERATOR

In digital computer design the need often arises for a method whereby a certain number of pulses can be applied to flip-flops, counters, adders, or other devices. Thus, a circuit must be used which has a gating characteristic wherein a continuous stream of pulses from a generator is applied to a gating network, so that when the gate is opened for a predetermined time, a certain number of pulses will be available at the output. Methods for doing this have been mentioned earlier with respect to the start-stop multivibrator and the flip-flop circuit to open or close an and-gate. Another method for doing this is shown in Fig. 4-12, which consists of a clock pulse generator, a flip-flop stage, an and-gate, and a delay line.

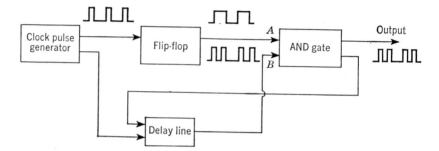

Fig. 4-12. Pulse burst generating system.

The output pulses from the generator are applied simultaneously to the flip-flop circuit and the delay line. When the first pulse enters the flip-flop stage, it triggers the flip-flop with the result that the output will be a steady positive voltage until the flip-flop is reset again. This steady-state positive voltage applied to the and-gate terminal *A* will provide an open gate condition for any pulses arriving at *B*. The first pulse, having also entered the delay line, arrives at the *B*-input of the and-gate at a later time, but during the presence of the positive voltage at *A*. Hence, the pulse from the delay line enters the and-gate and appears at the output. If, at this time, another pulse arrives at the flip-flop from the generator, the flip-flop stage is reset, the negative output voltage closes the and-gate and no longer permits any pulses to get through to the output terminal. Upon the arrival of the third pulse at the flip-flop stage from the generator, the flip-flop stage is reset and the whole process is repeated. Thus, the output consists of burst intervals which contain two pulses during each burst. If the delay time of the delay line is made shorter, more pulses will appear at the output during the burst time interval. Hence, a system can be designed to contain a certain amount of pulses during burst interval by regulating the constants of the delay line and the repetition frequency of the pulses procured from the pulse generator.

Questions Relating to Chapter 4

1. Draw a diode type and-circuit, and indicate which are the input terminals and which is the output terminal.

2. Briefly explain under what conditions there will be an output pulse from a diode and-circuit with respect to input pulses at one or more of the input terminals.

3. Compare the transistor and-circuit with the vacuum tube type in terms of component parts, etc.

4. What controls the current through the common load resistor of the transistor and-circuit?

5. Explain how a flip-flop circuit can be used in conjunction with an and-circuit to form a gating-in or gating-out device.

6. Draw a vacuum tube or-circuit, and indicate which are the input terminals and which is the output terminal.

7. Briefly explain under what conditions there will be an output from a transistor or-circuit with respect to input pulses at one or more of the input terminals.

8. Draw an inhibitor circuit, and indicate which are the input terminals and which is the output terminal. Label the inhibitory pulse.

9. Briefly explain under what conditions there will be an output from the foregoing circuit with respect to input pulses at one or more of the input terminals.

10. Briefly explain how a pulse burst generating system is used for the production of a specific number of pulses in an output group.

5

□ □ □
□ ■ □
□ □ □

Calculation Circuits

As with an office calculating machine, the digital computer device must be designed to perform various calculations such as addition, subtraction, multiplication, and division. Several combinations of circuits can be used for any particular arithmetic function. In the additive process, for instance, several varieties and combinations of circuits can be used, depending on whether a serial train or parallel train of binary numbers is involved. There are a number of circuit combinations which will perform multiplication, subtraction, or any other mathematical operation. Design also depends on whether transistors, germanium diodes, or vacuum tubes are employed, though often a sequence of virtually identical circuits can be used to construct a particular adder or subtracter. All in all, however, a great variety of circuit combinations exists.

For the newcomer to the field it is not necessary to understand or be familiar with each particular method employed in the numerous computers on the market. It is well, however, to have a thorough grounding in at least a few typical and representative types so as to comprehend the manner in which basic logic circuits are used to make up the calculation systems. With a thorough understand-

124

ing of the basic types presented herein, the reader will have acquired the necessary background for analysis and comprehension of any specific type of computer by a certain manufacturer that he may encounter later, since all use the basic ideas detailed in this chapter.

Depending on the scope of the device, a given digital computer may employ one or more adders, as well as one or more subtracters and multipliers. By use of a number of such circuits, simultaneous calculations of subtraction, addition, and multiplication can be performed. For instance, it may be necessary to perform two or three subtractions at one time, and the remainders from these calculations may have to be added together in an adder and later multiplied by some other number. There are various types of adders, subtracters, and multipliers, and the basic circuits involved in each of these calculations is discussed herein. Some are used in handling serial-train binary numbers, and others are employed for parallel-train numbers.

ADDERS

Adders in digital computers perform additions of two or more numbers by using combinations of or-circuits, and-circuits, and not-circuits. As with the use of decimal numbers for addition, in the binary system it is necessary to carry a number in the addition process as explained earlier. It is this carry function which adds complexity to the design of an adder in the digital computer systems. If it were not for the necessity of carrying, a simple or-circuit could be used to add the binary sum of 01 and 10 for example. Since an or-circuit will have an output for a signal appearing at either or both of its inputs, it would perform simple additive operations.

Adders are designed to be actuated by a group of pulses which represents a binary number rather than a train of pulses having a decimal count such as two pulses for the number 2, five pulses for 5, etc., such as may be employed in a basic flip-flop counter. In some adders, a sequential series of pulses is inserted, while other adders will accept pulses in parallel form, but the pulses have spaces representing the absence of pulses to indicate zeros. Thus, a train of pulses such as shown at (A) of Fig. 5-1 would represent the binary number shown at (B). It is such a binary pulse number which is inserted into an adder in conjunction with one or more ad-

(A)

(B)   1   0   1   1   0   1

Fig. 5-1. Pulse group and binary equivalent.

ditional binary pulse groups for addition. An example of this is shown in Fig. 5-2 in which an or-circuit is employed as a simple

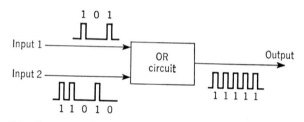

Fig. 5-2. Or-circuit forms simple adder with no "carry" ability.

(though incomplete) adder. Here, a pulse train represented by two pulses with a long interval between represents the binary number 101. At input No. 2, three pulses are inserted to represent the binary number 11010. Since an or-circuit will have an output for either or both input signals, the train of pulses at the output of the or-circuit will consist of 5 pulses, any 2 pulses having an equal interval between them as compared to the others. While the output in serial representation may then appear to be the decimal number 5, it actually is the binary number 11111 which represents 31 in its decimal equivalent. Similarly, if 101 is applied to input No. 1 and 1000 is applied to input No. 2, the output train of pulses would indicate 1101, the 0 being represented by the absence of a pulse and hence a longer time interval between the two pulses between which there is a 0.

While such an or-circuit can perform additions when there is no necessity for "carrying" a number, it is inadequate when the carrying function is necessary during the addition process. Hence, other circuits must be combined with the or-circuit to perform the additive function. To simplify the explanation, a *partial adder* is shown at (A) of Fig. 5-3. Such a partial adder is sometimes referred to as

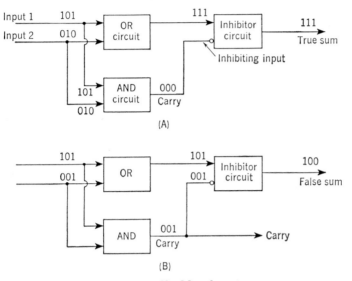

Fig. 5-3. Half-adder function.

a *half-adder*. As shown at (A), if the binary number 101 is applied to input No. 1, and the binary number 010 is applied to input No. 2, the output from the or-circuit would be the binary number 111 which, at this stage, is already the true sum of the two input numbers. The two input binary numbers are also applied to an and-circuit, and since an and-circuit must have a pulse present at both inputs in order to provide an output pulse, the output from the and-circuit will be zero as shown. Hence, the binary number 111, when applied to the inhibitor circuit, will appear at the output since no inhibitory pulse had been applied to the input.

At (B) of Fig. 5-3 the half-adder is again shown, but this time the binary number 101 applied to input 1 which is to be added to the binary number 001 applied to input 2. In this instance, the first place digits should add to 0 with one digit carried to the second place. The or-circuit will have an output of 101, since it will have an output for either or both of the input signals. The and-circuit, however, will have an output only if two pulses are present at the inputs simultaneously. Hence, the output from the and-circuit consists of the binary number 001. When these two are applied to the inhibitor circuit as shown, the 001 from the and-circuit inhibits the first place digit from the or-circuit, and hence the output from the inhibitor circuit consists of the binary number 100. This is a false sum or answer, and this false sum, in addition to the "carry" binary number from the and-circuit, must be processed further by the adder in order to obtain the true sum. This is done by use of a delay line in conjunction with another half-adder as shown in Fig. 5-4. The delay line will delay a binary bit by one place, and hence moves all digits one place to the left. Note that the output from the second half-adder is recirculated back into the delay line. Hence, whenever there is an output from the *second* half-adder, it is delayed by an additional *place* and recirculated into the input of the second half-adder as shown at (A) of Fig. 5-4.

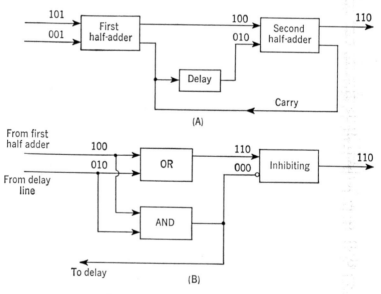

Fig. 5-4. Full-adder function.

Since the output from the first half-adder is 100 as shown at (A) of Fig. 5-4, this same output would be present at the input to the second half-adder. At the same time, the 001 *carry sum* from the half-adder is applied to the delay line and delayed for a time interval equal to one pulse. Hence, the delay line applies the binary number 010 to the second half-adder. The second half-adder is illustrated in complete block diagram form at (B) of Fig. 5-4 to illustrate the process involved. The output of 100 from the first half-adder is applied to the input of the or-circuit, and the output from the delay line (010) is applied to the second input of the or-circuit. The foregoing numbers are also applied to the and-circuit as shown. The output from the or-circuit will thus be 110 while the output from the and-circuit will be 000, since no two pulses are present at the input of the and-circuit at any given time. Thus, there are no inhibitory pulses applied to the inhibitor circuit and the binary sum 110 is present at the output. This represents the *true sum* of the numbers applied to the input of the full-adder.

The foregoing example required no recirculation since only one carry operation was required. When several carry operations are needed, however, the carry pulse from the second half-adder is recirculated several times as the following will illustrate.

At (A) of Fig. 5-5 the input to a full-adder consists of the binary number 111, which is to be added to the binary number 011. The

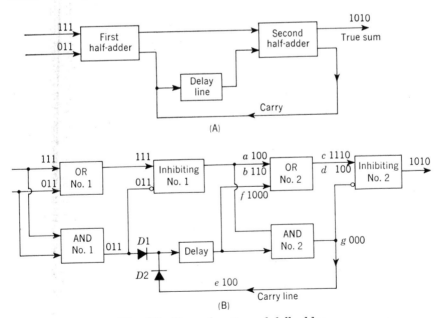

Fig. 5-5. Carry function of full-adder.

addition of these two numbers necessitates that the circuit add the two first place digits to produce 0 with one digit to carry. In the second place digits, the carry digit plus the two digits in the input numbers would equal 1 with 1 to carry to the third place. The third place addition of the two digits would result in 0 with another digit to carry to the fourth place, producing the true sum of 1010. Here, it can be seen that it is necessary to carry a number from the first place to the fourth place successively. The manner in which this is done can be seen from the illustration at (B) of Fig. 5-5, wherein all the blocks of the full-adder are illustrated.

When the binary numbers 111 and 011 are applied to the or-circuit, the output will be 111, since the or-circuit will produce an output for either or both of the input signals. When, however, the two binary numbers are applied to the and-circuit, only the two first place numbers appear, since the third place digit input to the and-circuit has no corresponding input to produce an output pulse. Thus, the output from the and-circuit consisting of 011 and the output from the or-circuit consisting of 111 are applied to the inhibiting circuit No. 1. The output from the and-circuit produces two inhibitory pulses and hence limits the output from the inhibitor circuit to the binary number marked A, consisting of 100. However, the output of 011 from the first and-circuit is applied to a delay circuit, and at the output of the delay circuit this number is 110 (marked B in the drawing). The A and B signals are applied to the or-circuit No. 2, and the output from the latter is designated as C and consists of the number 1110. The inputs to the second or-circuit are also applied to the second and-circuit, and since only third place digits occur simultaneously, the output from the second and-circuit consists of the binary number 100 and is designated as D in the drawing. The latter is recirculated to the delay circuit, and appears at the output of the delay circuit as the F binary number of 1000. Since this fourth place digit will go through the or-circuit, it contributes the fourth place digit to the C output of the or-circuit. Because the fourth place digit in the F number cannot enter the second and-circuit (since there is no corresponding digit occurring at that time), there is no further output from the second and-circuit. Hence, the input binary numbers to the second inhibitor circuit consist of the C number 1110 and the D number 100. Since this D number has only a third place digit, the latter acts as an inhibitory pulse for the third place digit of the C number and will cancel this third place digit from the output of the second inhibitor circuit. Thus, the output of the inhibitor circuit consists of 1010 which is the true sum of the two binary numbers applied to the input of the full-adder. Diode $D1$ is to prevent the carry pulses from entering the first inhibiting circuit. Diode $D2$ is to prevent signals from the first and-circuit from entering the carry line and reaching the second inhibitor circuit.

The full-adder will take any two numbers and add them together, regardles of the number of digits in either of the input numbers applied to the full-adder. Because of the recirculation of the carry signal in the delay line, it can perform the carry function for an infinite number of places from the first place on up.

The limitation of this particular adding system is that it has only two inputs and hence will accept only two serial train binary number groups at any one time. If many numbers are to be added, however, the same adder can be used over and over, or the accumulator type of adding device can be employed as discussed elsewhere herein. The particular type of adder system employed by a digital computer depends on the scope and limitations built into a particular machine. As with all computers, additional flexibility usually entails an increase in circuitry, with an added increase in the cost factor as well as the space occupied by the complete machine. Typical commercial computers, with some discussion of limitations and capabilities, are described in Chapter 8.

THE PARALLEL ADDER

The adders previously discussed employed an input consisting of a serial train representation of binary numbers, and an output also in serial train form. Another type of adder, which accommodates a parallel representation of binary numbers, can be made up of the basic flip-flop trigger type of circuit. In contrast to the counter type of flip-flop system discussed earlier, however, the circuits employed for the parallel binary representation consist of a

series of flip-flop circuits which have another input in addition to
the one shown previously. The basic circuit is shown in Fig. 5-6,
and is similar to the two stage counter discussed earlier (Chapter 3,

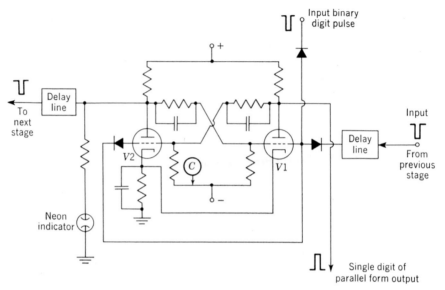

Fig. 5-6. Circuit for parallel addition and storage.

Fig. 3-7). The germanium diodes shown are for the purpose of preventing a short circuit of the grid voltage across the input system,
as well as providing a one-way low resistance path for the input
signal, while providing a high resistance path in the reverse direction. As before, the sequence of circuitry is shown from right to
left for simplicity of explanation, since this method conforms to the
value of the place numbers from right to left. Some commercial
schematics may, on occasion, show a series of flip-flops connected
together with the input at the left and the output at the right.

Each circuit is connected to a subsequent circuit through a delay line as opposed to the simple capacity coupling indicated for
the circuits described earlier. Thus, when this circuit registers "1"
because of tube V2 being in a nonconducting state, a triggering
pulse will trip over the circuit and produce a negative triggering
pulse for the next stage. This pulse, however, is delayed by one
binary place. The reason for the delay circuit will become more

evident from an inspection of Fig. 5-7 which shows four such stages hooked together in block diagram form. As shown, the initial entry may be a parallel binary number consisting of 0101. When this is

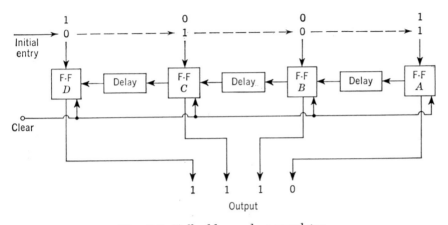

Fig. 5-7. Full-adder and accumulator.

entered into the individual circuits, the flip-flop circuit marked A and the circuit marked C would each register "1." This adder will now store the binary number for as long a period as the voltages are applied to the tubes. This device will also act as an adder since the entry of another number will cause the state of the flip-flops to change. If, for instance, the binary number 1001 is now entered in parallel form, it would cause circuit A to flip over and the latter would send a pulse to circuit B, causing it in turn to register "1." When the circuit A is flipped over, however, it would register "0." The entry of a single digit into the D circuit flips over the latter, and hence the new sum will be 1110, which represents the sum of the binary numbers 101 and 1001.

The purpose for the delay lines is to prevent premature tripping. Assume that the number 11 has been entered into the circuit in parallel form. In the latter case both A and B circuits would register the digit 1. If another number 11 were now entered into the system (one digit to the A circuit and one digit to the B circuit), the A circuit would trip to 0 and send a pulse to the B circuit. To prevent the latter pulse from entering the B circuit *at the same time a pulse is also entering at the top input,* the delay line is utilized. Thus, the 1 representing the second binary number applied to circuit B would enter the circuit and flip it over, and the B circuit would now be in readiness for the pulse from the A circuit when it arrives from the delay line. The delayed pulse now trips circuit B to generate a pulse for application to circuit C. After the latter circuit has been tripped, the counter would indicate 110, representing the sum of the binary numbers 11 plus 11.

This adder storage system would now hold the sum of the two numbers applied to it until all stages are cleared. Clearing can be accomplished by opening the grid circuit to the second tube of each flip-flop or applying a clearing pulse as shown earlier. Upon the application of a clearing process simultaneously to all stages, the output would be available as a parallel group of numbers. This is shown in Fig. 5-6, which indicates that a positive pulse is available from the plate of V1 when the circuit is cleared. If, of course, the circuit has not stored a number, the stage will not flip over and in consequence there would be no output from the anode of V1. When the stage represents 0, V2 is in a conducting state and the removal of the negative potential at the grid of V2 during the clearing process would not cause the tube to cut off, and will not change the stable state. When the stage registers 1, however, V2 is nonconducting and hence the grid is at cut-off. Upon removal of the negative voltage at the grid of V2, the stage would change its stable state and clear to 0.

THE SUBTRACTER

One method for performing subtraction in digital computers is by a circuit combination of inhibitor circuits and adders. The basic inhibitor circuit alone can perform some subtracting functions, but will produce false answers when it is necessary to "borrow" a number from the next place in order to perform the subtraction process. The fundamental subtracting process of an inhibiting circuit is shown at (A) of Fig. 5-8. Here, the first input to the inhibitor circuit consists of the minuend, 111. The subtrahend, or number to be subtracted, is 101 and is applied to the second input of the inhibitor circuit, as shown. Because the first and third place digits of the subtrahend act as *inhibitory* pulses, they prevent the first and third place digits of the minuend from going through the circuit. Hence, only the second place digit of the minuend appears at the output, and thus the output represents the true remainder of the subtraction process and equals 10.

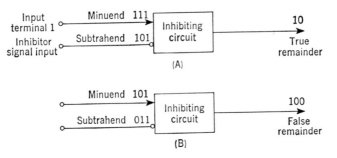

Fig. 5-8. Basic subtracter, using an inhibiting circuit.

As with the half-adder, simple computations can be performed with the inhibitor; but when it is necessary to borrow, other circuits are necessary. In the subtraction process the inability of the inhibiting circuit to provide the true remainder is shown at (B) of Fig. 5-8, where the first input to the circuit consists of the minuend 101 from which is to be subtracted the number shown at the second input, consisting of the subtrahend 11. Since the first and second place digits of the subtrahend act as inhibitory pulses, the first place digit of the minuend will not appear at the output of the inhibitor circuit. Hence, the output consists of 100 which is a false remainder of the subtraction process, since the correct answer should be 10.

To obtain a correct answer for "carry" conditions it is necessary to utilize the circuit shown at (A) of Fig. 5-9, consisting of three inhibiting circuits, an adder, and a delay line. Here, the minuend of 11 is applied to the first input of the first inhibitor circuit, and the subtrahend of 01 is applied to the second input of the first inhibitor circuit, as shown. Two inputs are also applied to the second inhibitor circuit, but are inverted. Thus, the subtrahend is used as the inhibitory factor for the first inhibitor circuit, while the minuend is used as the inhibitory factor for the second inhibitor circuit. In the first inhibitor circuit, the inhibitory subtrahend pulse limits the output from the first inhibitor circuit to 10. In the second inhibitor circuit the minuend inhibits the subtrahend input with the result that there is zero output from the inhibitor circuit. The

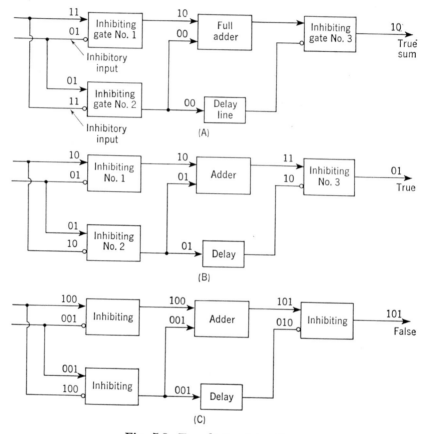

Fig. 5-9. Two-digit subtraction.

number 10 applied to the full-adder and to the third inhibitor circuit will not be inhibited, and will appear at the output as the true remainder of the subtraction process.

At (B) the subtracter is reproduced again to indicate the process involved for the subtraction of 01 from 10. The output from the first inhibitor circuit will be 10, since the solitary first place inhibitory pulse has nothing to cancel at that time. At the second inhibitor circuit, the inhibitory pulse again occurs at a time when there is no pulse present at the first input to the second inhibitor circuit, and hence the output from the second inhibitor circuit will be 01. These two numbers are applied to a full-adder and appear at the output as 11. The number 01 from the second inhibitor circuit is also applied to a delay line and appears at the output of the latter as 10. This is applied to the third inhibitor circuit in conjunction with the output from the adder. The second place digit at the second input to the third inhibitor circuit inhibits the second place digit at the first input of the third inhibitor circuit, and in consequence the output of the latter consists of 01, which is the true remainder.

The subtracter shown at (A) or (B) of Fig. 5-9 is known as a two digit subtracter, because it cannot borrow beyond a two digit input for the minuend and subtrahend. If, for instance, the subtraction process indicated at (C) of Fig. 5-9 were to be carried out, a false remainder would occur because of the inability of the circuit to borrow the numbers necessary to perform the subtraction process. In this illustration, the number 100 is the minuend and 001 the subtrahend. When these are applied to the first inhibitor circuit they appear at the output as 100, since the inhibitory first place pulse finds no pulse to inhibit. The output from the lower second inhibitor circuit will be 001, since the third place pulse in the inhibitory input finds no other pulse to cancel. The two binary numbers applied to the adder result in an output of 101. The output from the second inhibitor circuit consisting of 001 is applied to a delay line and appears as 010, which in conjunction with the output from the adder is applied to the third inhibitor circuit. Since the second place inhibitory pulse does not affect the 101 input to the third inhibitor circuit, the latter number appears at the output and represents a false remainder of the subtraction process.

To increase the number of places which can be handled by the

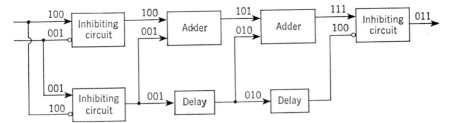

Fig. 5-10. Circuits necessary for increasing subtraction process.

subtracter with respect to the minuend and subtrahend during the subtraction process, additional circuits would have to be employed. For handling three digits, the original two digit subtracter would have to have the added circuits shown in Fig. 5-10. Additional circuits, however, increase the cost and size of the subtracter, and for this reason other means are usually employed to eliminate the necessity for the construction of a complex subtracter unit.

Subtracters and adders can be combined when it is necessary to perform calculations involving both subtraction and addition. For instance, two subtraction problems can be fed simultaneously into the system shown at (A) of Fig. 5-11. Here, the subtrahend 11

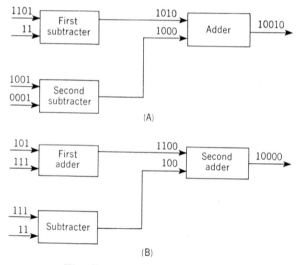

Fig. 5-11. Multiple subtraction.

is to be subtracted from the minuend 1101 while at the same time a second subtrahend 01 is to be subtracted from 1001. By employing two subtracters as shown, each subtracter performs its individual function; the first subtracter produces a remainder of 1010 and the second subtracter produces a remainder of 1000. If these two sums are now to be added together, a full-adder can be used as shown; or if the number from the second subtracter is to be subtracted from the number from the first subtracter, a third subtracter can be employed.

Simultaneous addition and subtraction can also be employed by combining adders and subtracters as shown at (B) of Fig. 5-11. Here, the binary number 11 is to be subtracted from 111, and the remainder subtracted from the sum of 101 plus 111. Hence, the latter two numbers are applied to an adder which produces the sum of 1100, and the subtraction process of 11 from 111 produces the binary number 100. The latter number can be subtracted from the binary number 1100 by use of another subtracter, or it can be added by using an adder as shown in the illustration.

Other combinations can be employed, though often particular sums or products are rerouted through the computer as required to produce the final sum. The allocation of the various numbers of a particular problem to the individual circuits of the computer must be established by the program of instructions which are set up beforehand for the particular problem involved. Typical illustrations of this process are shown in Chapter 7.

The subtraction process can be simplified considerably in digital computers by employing the nines complement principle. In order to understand how this principle is applied to binary notation, it is necessary to examine first the nines complement process as applied to decimal notation. The process involved consists of changing the subtrahend (the number to be subtracted) and then employing an addition process. This can be better understood by analyzing a typical example. For instance, assume that 2341 is to be subtracted from 7465 to produce a remainder of 5124 as follows:

$$
\begin{array}{r}
7465 \\
-2341 \\
\hline
5124
\end{array}
$$

The subtrahend is now changed by subtracting each digit from 9. Thus, 2341 becomes 7658 because 2 from 9 is 7, 3 from 9 is 6, etc. This changed subtrahend is now *added* to the minuend as follows:

$$
\begin{array}{r}
7465 \\
+7658 \\
\hline
15123
\end{array}
$$

The leading digit in the remainder shown above (the digit 1) is now shifted to the units position and added, getting the correct answer as shown below:

$$\begin{array}{r} 7465 \\ +7658 \\ \hline 1\,5123 \\ +1 \\ \hline 5124 \end{array}$$

In the foregoing, the process of shifting the leading 1 to the units position is known as *end-around carry*. The following is another example of the entire process:

$$\begin{array}{r} 53682 \\ -52620 \\ \hline 1062 \end{array} \qquad \begin{array}{r} 53682 \\ +47379 \\ \hline 1\,01061 \\ +1 \\ \hline 1062 \end{array}$$

The foregoing, which involves nines complementing, can also be applied to binary notation in terms of *ones complementing*. Here, the process is much more simple because the subtrahend need not be subtracted from 9, since the base-two system is employed. Instead, the minuend is simply inverted; that is, each 0 is changed to 1 and each 1 is changed to 0. For instance, if the number 101(5) is to be subtracted from 1101 (13), the remainder would be 1000 (8). The following shows the ones complementing process with the end-around carry:

$$\begin{array}{r} 1101 \\ -0101 \\ \hline 1000 \end{array} \qquad \begin{array}{r} 1101 \\ +1010 \\ \hline 1\,0111 \\ +1 \\ \hline 1000 \end{array}$$

When subtracting, the subtrahend must have as many binary digits (0 and 1) as are in the minuend, or an error will result during the ones complementing process. Even though in normal binary subtraction both answers would be the same if the subtrahend were not filled out, an error would result in the ones complementing process. This can be proved by subjecting the two examples shown below to the ones complementing process:

	Incorrect	Correct
	11110	11110
	−1011	01011
	10011	10011

The following is an additional example to help illustrate the ones complementing process:

$$
\begin{array}{ll}
10110 \ (22) & 10110 \\
\underline{-01011 \ (11)} \quad = & \underline{+10100} \\
1011 \ (11) & 1\ 01010 \\
& \underline{+1} \\
& 1011
\end{array}
$$

While the process may appear complex in terms of applications to computers, it is actually simpler to convert a digit 1 to 0 and vice versa in terms of the electronic circuitry in computers than to employ circuit combinations which must have the ability to borrow numbers. Binary numbers can be inverted (complemented) by utilizing conventional inverting circuits.

A conventional amplifier circuit as previously discussed has the ability to provide a phase reversal, and is used as the basic inverting circuit. Such an inverter is usually preceded by a cathode follower input, and the output from the inverter amplifier is fed to a cathode follower with diode clamp circuits. The inverter circuits thus act to complement a number by changing the digit 1 to 0 and vice versa. The inverter may be used in conjunction with and-gates, as shown in Fig. 5-12, so that either the complement can be procured from a number or the original number gated through for other purposes. As shown, for instance, if 0101 is applied to the inverter it would appear as 1010 at the top and-gate. There will be no output from this and-gate unless pulses are applied to the second input of this and-gate. The pulses would consist of a continuous stream and would open the and-gate only when coinciding pulses are present. The lower and-gate is pulsed at its second input when the original signal is to be gated through. The output from the and-gates is applied to an or-circuit which will pass either the signal from the upper and-gate or the signal from the lower and-gate.

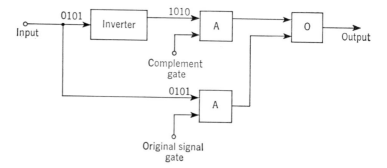

Fig. 5-12. Complement circuitry.

MULTIPLIERS

One method for doing a multiplication problem is to add the multiplicand to itself by the number of times indicated by the multiplier. Thus, if 438 is to be multiplied by 65, the multiplicand of 438 can be added together 65 times to obtain the product. This is a simple method of performing the multiplication in digital computers without the necessity for complex circuitry, the only drawback being that it takes longer for the calculation to be performed with respect to the speed of the addition and subtraction processes by the methods previously detailed. While the repetitive addition of the multiplicand is employed in some digital computers, others employ circuitry which will solve the multiplication in the same manner that it is done in the arithmetic formula of procuring partial products and adding the latter together. There are several circuit combinations which can be employed for performing the multiplication process in this manner. As with adders and subtracters, special circuit combinations are necessary to perform the functions of offsetting the multiplicand by the number of places required during the initial adding process. After this has been done, adders must be utilized to procure the sum of the offset multiplicand numbers. The multipliers must be designed to handle binary numbers, where both the multiplicand and multiplier are inserted simultaneously into the multiplier, or fit into the multiplier at a different time interval.

The requirements of a multiplier can be better understood by examining a typical problem:

$$
\begin{array}{r}
111 \ (7) \\
\times 11 \ (3) \\
\hline
111 \\
111 \\
\hline
10101 \ (21)
\end{array}
$$

In the foregoing example, the multiplicand 111 (7) is to be multiplied by 11 (3). This means that the multiplicand must be set down twice, with the second multiplicand moved to the left by one place as in regular multiplication. When these two figures are added together, the result is 10101 (21). Hence, it is obvious that a multiplier must use the multiplicand for addition purposes in the manner as indicated by the number of binary digits in the multiplier. In the example just given, the multiplier indicated that the multiplicand had to be added to another number equal to the multiplicand but moved over one place. After the multiplier does this, it is also necessary to feed the original multiplicand, plus the delayed multiplicand, into an adder so that the sum can be procured. Actually, the adder would receive at one input the binary number 111 representing the initial multiplicand, and then the binary number 1110, representing the displaced or delayed multiplicand.

The foregoing was a simple example of multiplication, but the multiplier must also be capable of displacing the multiplicand initially in such instances where the multiplier ends in a 0. This type of multiplication is represented by the following:

$$
\begin{array}{r}
111 \ (7) \\
\times 10 \ (2) \\
\hline
000 \\
111 \\
\hline
1110 \ (14)
\end{array}
$$

Here, the multiplicand again consists of 111 (7) but now the multiplier is 10 (2). Hence, the multiplier must delay the multiplicand by a one place interval and then add the delayed mutiplicand so that the answer is 1110 (14).

Another instance where a combination of the two foregoing conditions occur is the following:

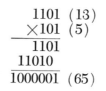

$$1101 \quad (13)$$
$$\underline{\times 101} \quad (5)$$
$$1101$$
$$11010$$
$$\overline{1000001} \quad (65)$$

In the foregoing, the binary number 101 representing the multiplier now has 0 between the first and third place digits. Thus, the multiplicand must be set down once, then delayed by a two place interval and set down again. These two figures must then be added to produce the product shown. From the foregoing it is evident that the multiplier must be such that any combination of binary digits or 0's, in either the multiplier or the multiplicand, would be taken care of automatically.

PRESET MULTIPLIER

Multiplication can be performed in a comparatively simple manner if the binary number represented by the multiplier is preset manually by switches prior to the application of the multiplicand to the multiplier circuits. This is shown in Fig. 5-13. Here, several

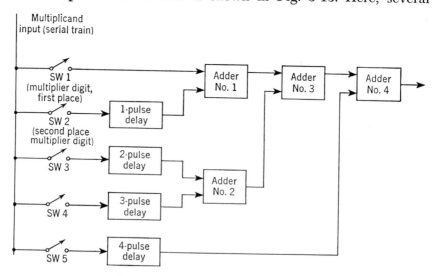

Fig. 5-13. Use of switches for multiplication.

adders and delay circuits are employed in combination with a number of switches. The number of switches necessary depends on the number of digits which will be encountered in the multiplier. Regardless of the number of switches for the multiplier, however, the multiplicand can have an infinite number of digits since the multiplicand has no limitations imposed on it by this circuit.

As shown in Fig. 5-13, the first switch closes the circuit for the first adder. The second and successive switches are applied to a series of delay lines respectively. The second switch is applied to a delay line which will delay the input by a one pulse (one digit) duration. The third switch is applied to a delay line which delays the input by a two pulse duration, etc. The output from the first delay line is applied to the first adder and the output from the other delay lines to the successive adders as shown.

For the principle of operation, assume that the multiplicand is 111 and the multiplier 11, as in the first example given in this discussion. In such an instance, switch 1 and switch 2 are closed, and the multiplicand representing three sequential pulses (7) is applied to the multiplicand input shown in Fig. 5-13. Since the first two switches are closed, the multiplicand is applied to the first adder immediately. Since the second switch is also closed, the multiplicand is applied to the delay circuit which delays the input serial train of pulses by one pulse duration. Hence, at the output from the first delay line the binary serial train multiplicand will lag the multiplicand inserted at the A input of the first adder by one pulse displacement. Thus, the offset function of the multiplication process has been satisfied, and the output from the first adder will now consist of the product of 111 multiplied by 11, since the input to the first adder at A consisted of 111 and the input at B of the first adder consisted of 1110.

The additional adders are necessary in instances where there are more than two binary digits in the multiplier, and their applications will be discussed later. In the example just discussed the output from the first adder is actually the true product, and this would be applied to one of the inputs of adder No. 3. Since there is no other input to this adder, the true product will appear at its output, be applied to the fourth adder, and appear at its output also, since there is but one input to the fourth adder. Thus, when there are only two numbers in the multiplier, the other adders are not necessary, but at the same time do not hamper the operations of the multiplier because they do not alter or disturb the proper pulse sequence representing the true product.

If the multiplicand is again 111, but the multiplier is 10, such as discussed previously for the second example, only switch No. 2 of the preset multiplier is closed. The first switch is left open since there is no first place digit. Thus, the multiplicand, when applied to the input, will enter the first delay line and will appear at the output of the adder as 1110.

If the multiplicand consists of 1101 and the multiplier 101, as in the third example previously discussed, the first switch would be closed to represent the first place binary number of the multiplier. The second switch would be left open, since the second place of the multiplier is 0. The third switch would be closed, however, because of the third place digit in the multiplier. When the multiplicand is now applied to the input, it will appear at the A input of the first adder and also at the input of the two-pulse delay line. The output from the first adder thus consists of the binary number 1101 representing the undelayed multiplicand. The output from the second adder would be 110100, representing the multiplicand delayed by two places. Both the undelayed multiplicand and the two place delayed multiplicand are applied to the third adder, and the output from the latter would then be the true product of 1000001.

The utilization of all the switches would occur if the multiplier contained five digits as shown in the following example:

$$
\begin{array}{r}
11\ (3) \\
\times 11111\ (31) \\
\hline
11 \\
110 \\
1100 \\
11000 \\
110000 \\
\hline
1011101\ (93)
\end{array}
$$

In the above example it can be seen that the multiplication process necessitates that the multiplicand be set down five times, with each successive multiplicand displaced by one additional digit interval, and then all added together to procure the product. In this instance, all the switches would be closed and the multiplicand applied to the input. To the first adder the multiplicand would be applied at A without delay, and at B delayed by one place. The second adder receives the multiplicand delayed by two places, and three; the sum would be applied to the input of the third adder in conjunction with the output from the first adder. Thus, the first adder supplies to the third adder the binary number 1001 and the second adder supplies to the third adder the binary number 100100. The third adder adds these two together to produce 101101, and the latter is supplied to the fourth adder in addition to the multiplicand delayed by four places. Hence, the inputs to the fourth adder consist of 101101 and 110000. The sum of these two figures equals 1011101 and represents the true product.

In the foregoing example, it is evident that any two numbers can be multiplied, as long as the multiplier does not contain more than five binary digits. The switches can be in the form of push buttons, and arranged from right to left to represent the binary places of the multiplier. The switches can be of the type which are closed when pushed once and open when pushed again, so that the multiplier can be cleared before it is preset for the next multiplication. Only those switches are depressed which represent the binary digits of the multiplier, and when there are 0's in the multiplier the switches are left open. Thus, if 101 (5) is to be multiplied by 10001 (17), only the first and fifth switches would be depressed to represent the two single digits in the multiplier, and the multiplicand would be applied to the input. Thus, the multiplicand would be applied to the first adder and the fourth delay line only, and appear as 1010101 (85). (Input devices are detailed in Chapter 7.) In practice, the push buttons are replaced by electronic switching devices or gates for high speed calculation, the actuating signals for the multiplier being supplied from storage or from accumulators.

If it is necessary to perform calculations where more than five digits are involved in the multiplier, it would be necessary to add additional delay lines to delay the binary train by five places, six places, etc. The output from other delays would necessitate additional adders in a pattern similar to the preset multiplier shown.

SHIFT REGISTERS

As detailed for the preset multiplier, the multiplicand is shifted by the proper amounts to the left, and then the addition process provides the products of the multiplication. Multiplication can, of course, be performed without shifting; the multiplicand can be added to itself the number of times signified by the multiplier. In office adding machines, the process would take considerable time if a large number of digits were involved in the multiplier, though in electronic computers, the repetitive addition of a number of multiplicands can be done in a relatively short interval.

Even in digital computers, however, the process of multiplication can be speeded up considerably by using the shift method, since the multiplicand need be added only according to the number of digits in the multiplier rather than by the *sum* represented by the digits. For this reason many computers utilize automatic shifting devices known as *shift registers*.

There are a variety of shift registers used in computers for shifting binary numbers either to the left or to the right. The left shifting is used in the multiplication process while the right shifting is employed in division. Some types of shift registers have already been discussed, a basic shifting device consisting of the ring counters illustrated in Fig. 3-11 and 3-12. The ring counter shifts a single digit through the ring as required, but the principles involved can also be employed for shifting a group of numbers. A basic right shift register is shown in Fig. 5-14, and resembles closely the ring counter previously discussed, except that inputs are provided to a group of the flip-flop stages for insertion of a group of numbers in parallel form. Three stages of flip-flop circuits are shown, though of course as many as desired could be used, and the output of the last can be applied to the first in ring fashion to permit shifting a number around several times if needed. This system can also be employed for left shifting, by reversing the input-output lines. A schematic of the left shift would be a mirror image of the one shown in Fig. 5-14.

Since the shift register illustrated in Fig. 5-14 functions in exactly the same manner as the ring counter, a review of the discussion for the latter topic will indicate the manner in which this device functions. Once a number has been inserted, a reset or shift pulse will clear a particular flip-flop and move the number to the

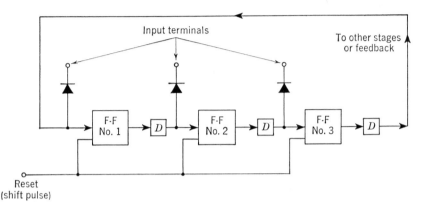

Fig. 5-14. Right shift register.

next stage. The delay lines prevent interaction from the pulse arriving from a previous flip-flop with that of the reset pulse. Thus, if the second flip-flop stage is in the "on" position, the shift pulse would change the state of the second flip-flop to zero and send a triggering pulse to the third flip-flop stage. If a shift pulse arrives at the third stage at the same time that the tripping pulse from the previous stage is applied, incorrect shifting would result. Thus, the delay line sends a tripping pulse to the next flip-flop after the shift pulse has performed its function.

Shift registers can be formed by other means, without the use of flip-flop circuits. One method for shifting numbers to the left is illustrated in the next topic, where and-gates and or-gates are employed to handle partial products.

PARALLEL-SHIFT MULTIPLIER

A multiplier with an automatic shift process is shown in Fig. 5-15. This particular system uses delay lines in conjunction with and-circuits and or-circuits as shown, and will handle a multiplicand of up to three digits, as well as a multiplier containing up to three digits as shown. The product is limited to a five digit answer. For a similar multiplier handling a larger number of digits in either the multiplier, multiplicand, or product, additional delay lines, and-circuits, and or-circuits have to be employed utilizing the same progressive interconnections as indicated in Fig. 5-15.

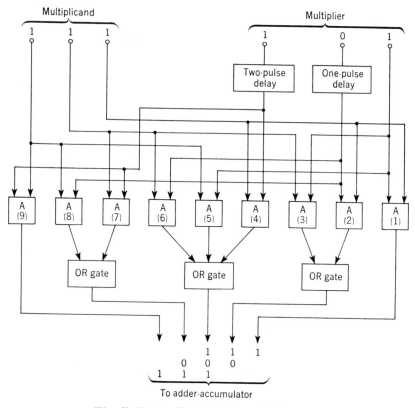

Fig. 5-15. Parallel shift in multiplication.

The multiplier pulse train is inserted in parallel form. The multiplicand is also a binary number in parallel form, though obtained from flip-flops which hold the input at a steady state; otherwise it would be necessary to have the multiplicand repeatedly gated in simultaneously with each pulse derived from the multiplier input and delay circuits.

Assume that the multiplicand consists of three binary digits, 111. This is a steady-state signal which represents an initial rise in positive potential and a holding of such positive potential as previously described for typical flip-flop characteristics. When a long duration pulse is applied to one input of an and-circuit there will be no output. If, however, a series of short duration pulses is applied to the other input of the and-circuit, the output will consist of a series of pulses which were gated in by the long duration positive pulse.

When the multiplicand number is applied to the three inputs at the left of Fig. 5-15 in a steady-state condition, the multiplier parallel-train binary number is applied to the three inputs at the right in Fig. 5-15. Inasmuch as the second place and third place pulses enter delay networks, the first place pulse will arrive at the and-circuit No. 1 prior to the other digits of the multiplier numbers. The and-circuit No. 1 derives one of its inputs from the first place multiplicand circuit, hence the and-circuit gate opens and a digit appears at the first place output below the multiplier system. The multiplier digit is also applied to one of the inputs of the third and-circuit as well as the fifth and-circuit. The other inputs to the third and fifth and-circuits are the second and third place digits of a multiplicand, respectively. Thus at the output, the second and third place digits of the first partial product are produced. Since no multiplier pulses enter the other and-circuits, there is no output from them.

The second place multiplier digit enters a one pulse delay and affects and-circuits No. 2, No. 6, and No. 8. An open gate condition would, therefore, re-enter the multiplicand, as a second partial product, shifted to the left by one digit. Since the second place multiplier digit is 0 in the example given in Fig. 5-15, however, there is no output for the second place shift.

The third digit of the multiplier is delayed by two pulses and is applied to and-circuits No. 4, No. 7, and No. 9. Since the latter and-circuits are also connected to the multiplicand input, it will create the open gate condition for the and-circuits No. 4, No. 7, and No. 9, and produce the third partial product at the output, shifted to the left by two places.

Thus, the circuit shown in Fig. 5-15 is, in effect, a shift register which will produce partial products and shift them to the left as required. The output, however, is not the *product* of the multiplication, but consists of only the *partial products* and hence the parallel groups of pulses which appear must be applied to an adder accumulator type circuit (see Fig. 5-7), which will take each partial product and add it to the previous one, for the true product:

$$
\begin{array}{ll}
111 & \text{First output} \\
000 & \text{Second output} \\
\underline{111} & \text{Third output} \\
100011 & \text{Adder output}
\end{array}
$$

Variations in multipliers and shift registers discussed herein will be encountered, but the foregoing types indicate the basic method of accomplishing multiplication, other than repeatedly adding the multiplicand by the number of times specified by the multiplier. As mentioned earlier, however, the process requires more time, and means must be taken for proper gating in of the multiplicand so that it will be added only the exactly required number of times.

As with other computer circuits discussed herein, the one illustrated in Fig. 5-15 can consist of diodes, vacuum tubes, or transistors. In most of the other schematics shown in this book, crossed lines which are not connected, have been indicated by a small loop. For the diagram in Fig. 5-15, however, crossed lines are shown without the loop while connected lines are shown with a heavy dot. This is the manner in which such block schematics will be typified in many of the manuals on computers, and the reader should become familiar with this method of representation.

DIVISION

A system which reduces the repetition rate of a serial train of pulses to a lower rate performs the general functions of a divider. A typical system is shown in Fig. 5-16, where the basic repetition rate is procured from a pulse generator. The latter furnishes a continuous stream of timed or clocked pulses having a fixed frequency rate per second. These pulses are applied to one of the inputs of an and-circuit as shown. Below the and-gate is shown a flip-flop which indicates the "on" and "off" conditions by the numerals 1 and 0. In block diagrams, this method of notating the respective "on" and "off" conditions is frequently used, and simplifies the method for indicating where the input pulses are applied (whether to the tube which is "on" or to the tube which is "off").

The flip-flop shown in Fig. 5-16 is in the "on" condition and applies to the and-circuit a positive polarity, permitting the entry into

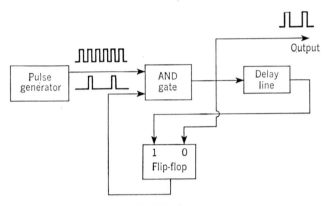

Fig. 5-16. Divider system.

the and-gate of a pulse from the generator. At the output of the and-gate the pulse is simultaneously applied to a delay line and to the "0" stage of the flip-flop. The pulse arriving at the flip-flop will reset the latter, with the result that the voltage output changes and thus closes the and-gate. Hence, no pulses will get through the and-gate until the flip-flop stage is triggered again. The pulse which entered the delay line comes out of this line at a later time interval and is applied to the flip-flop, resetting the latter and again providing an output voltage which will open the and-gate. Thus, another pulse enters the and-gate and the entire process is repeated.

The foregoing process results in a train of pulses at the output terminal which are of a lower repetition frequency than those from the pulse generator, but yet are accurately timed and synchronized with the generator. The repetition frequency (spacing of pulses) at the output is regulated primarily by the amount of delay introduced by the delay line. Changing the amount of delay will alter the ratio of repetition rate between the clock pulses from the generator and the output, but synchronization will be maintained. If the frequency of the pulses from the generator is changed, the ratio of generator pulses to output pulses will also change, because a change of frequency will alter delay time in a delay line with fixed constants.

In the foregoing system, a train of pulses is divided by a predetermined amount, and thus serves a useful purpose. There are occasions, however, when the division process must be applied to actual binary numbers for convenience. Hence, other processes must be evolved for accomplishing division besides the method outlined above.

Earlier it was mentioned that a simple method for performing multiplication was by repetitive addition of the multiplicand. In division, a simple method for performing the calculation consists of subtracting the divisor from the dividend repeatedly until there is no remainder or only a fractional remainder. The number of times which the divisor could be subtracted from the dividend would then be the answer or quotient.

Figure 5-17 illustrates the basic circuit for performing division by repeated subtraction. The dividend and divisor are inserted into

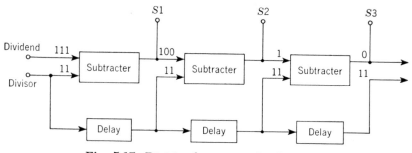

Fig. 5-17. Division by repeated subtraction.

a subtracter and the initial subtraction step is thus performed. The divisor is then channeled to a delay circuit so that it reappears at the input of the second subtracter with the same time delay as that encountered by the numbers entered into the first subtracter. Successive subtracters are then employed until the final result is 0 or a fractional number. The number of times that the divisor was subtracted from the dividend is then the quotient or answer to the division problem. Terminals S1, S2, S3, etc. comprise the indicators. All terminals preceding the one which indicates a 0 will register the quotient of the division process. These terminals must be channeled to a sensing device or indicating register to show the number of subtractions which were performed.

As with the multiplication process, however, the foregoing method of division entails a considerable amount of extra time over that which would result if circuitry were used to perform the division by the formula utilized in ordinary arithmetic. When using binary numbers in ordinary arithmetic, the divisor is placed below the dividend just as it is done in the decimal system, and the subtraction process results in a shifting of the divisor to the right for repeated divisions until the true answer or quotient has been procured. By this method, the greater number of repetitive subtractions of the divisor from the dividend is reduced considerably. For digital computer circuitry involving such division, it is necessary to have a shift register similar to that employed for multiplication, except that instead of shifting partial products to the left and performing additions, right shifting is employed. In such an instance it is necessary to shift the *divisor* to the right and perform a *subtraction* process. Thus, the division process is similar to the multiplication, except for the right shift instead of left, and the subtraction instead of addition. As with multiplication, however, the use of binary numbers limits the process to handling only 0 and 1 ("off" and "on" circuit conditions) as indicated by the typical example of dividing 111100 (60) by 100 (4). This gives an answer of 1111 (15):

$$
\begin{array}{r}
1111 \\
100{\overline{\smash{\big)}\,111100}} \\
\underline{100} \\
111 \\
\underline{100} \\
110 \\
\underline{100} \\
100 \\
\underline{100}
\end{array}
$$

Figure 5-18 shows the basic circuits employed for division using the right shift process. The dividend is applied to the first subtracter as shown, but the divisor is entered as displaced to the left so that it coincides with the initial digits of the dividend. The divisor is also entered into a shift register for progressive shifting of the divisor to the right. (A succession of delay lines could also be employed except that for shifts involving a number of digit displacements, an exorbitant pulse delay time would be necessary.)

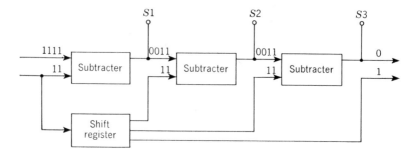

Fig. 5-18. Division using right shifting.

After the first subtracter, the remainder is entered into a second subtracter plus the shifted divisor as shown. Since the divisor (11) actually represents 110 in this instance because of its displacement, the subtracter must be of such a type that the number entered into the upper terminal will proceed through the circuit if the number to be subtracted is larger. Thus, the third subtracter receives 11 at each input, with the result that there is 0 output. Here, again, terminal indicators S1, S2, S3, etc. are employed to sense or indicate the number of subtractions which were performed.

Instead of shifting the divisor, the dividend can be progressively shifted to the left and the divisor remain fixed with respect to the relative mathematical place. The latter method is used in the IBM 650 Data Processing Computer. As previously mentioned, shifting combined with subtracting is employed. The dividend is progressively shifted to the left, one position at a time, and for each shift a portion of the dividend is repetitively reduced by the divisor. The number of subtraction processes which are required to reduce the dividend to a value less than the divisor is counted and registers in the computer as the quotient. With the IBM 650, division ends after the 10th shift. When the dividend exceeds ten digits, the problem is broken down into smaller components.

Virtually all digital computers utilize the subtraction and shift procedures for the division process. Variations consist in the type of shift register utilized, the method employed for sensing the number of divisions procured, and the number of successive subtractions of which the machine is capable.

COUNTERS

Counters are also used in arithmetic process as described in Chapter 3. In addition to the type counters discussed previously, counting can be done by taking advantage of the and-gate principles. A typical pulse counter of this type is shown in Fig. 5-19.

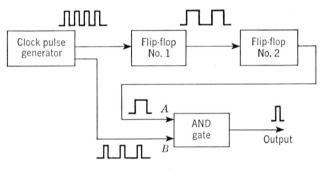

Fig. 5-19. Pulse counter.

This particular counter is made up of a series of flip-flop stages plus an and-gate for counting down a certain number of serial train pulses. Only two flip-flop circuits are shown, though as many as desired can be employed, depending on the amount of counting which is to be performed.

Pulses from the clock pulse generator are applied to the first flip-flop circuit. The pulses have a fixed repetition frequency, and as shown in Fig. 5-19, the generator also applies such pulses to the and-circuit. As mentioned earlier, a single flip-flop circuit can perform counting because it furnishes a single output pulse of a particular polarity for every two input pulses. The flip-flop circuit will provide a negative pulse during one triggering, and a positive pulse during another triggering. For this discussion it is assumed that only the positive pulses represent digits while negative pulses represent 0.

For a single flip-flop stage, this system will count to 2, while with two flip-flop stages it will count to 4. Similarly, three flip-flop stages will count to 6, four stages will count to 8, etc. The output from the second flip-flop is applied to the and-circuit as shown. In an and-circuit it is necessary for a pulse to be present at both the A and B inputs in order to procure an output. Hence, the output from the and-gate will consist of one pulse for every four pulses applied to the B input. By employing an and-circuit, the output pulses consist of the short duration type pulses procured from the clock pulse generator rather than the wider pulses obtained from flip-flop output stages.

Questions Relating to Chapter 5

1. Show in block diagram form the various circuits necessary to construct a partial or half-adder.

2. Show by block diagram the various circuits involved in the construction of a full-adder.

3. In the block diagram of the adder drawn for Question No. 2, indicate the binary number 101 as being applied to one input, and the binary number 100 applied to the other input. Show the progression of binary numbers through the full-adder.

4. What type of additive functions can be performed by the half-adder?

5. Is there any limit to the number of place digits of two binary numbers inserted into a full-adder?

6. Explain the purpose for delay lines in the parallel adder.

7. What basic circuit can perform subtraction functions but will produce false sums when borrowing is necessary?

8. Draw a block diagram of a two digit subtracter, and label the type of circuits used.

9. Explain how complementing can be used in the subtraction process. Illustrate with two examples.

10. Draw a block diagram of a preset multiplier and indicate the process involved when it is desired to multiply 1011 by 101 binary.

11. Explain the necessity for using a shift register in the multiplication circuitry of digital computers.

12. Draw a block diagram of a "right" shift register, using flip-flops and delay lines.

13. Describe one method for performing division in a digital computer.

14. Explain the operation of a pulse counter using two flip-flop stages and an and-gate.

6

□ □ □
□ □ ■
□ □ □

STORAGE SYSTEMS

INTRODUCTION

Digital computers use a number of methods for storing information for future use. In many instances the answers to calculations must be held in abeyance for several minutes, hours, or even days until other calculations are performed. When such other calculations have been completed, their results may have to be combined with results obtained from earlier calculations. Often, also, it is necessary to store different types of information in a computer so that such information can be procured from the computer at a later date and utilized as required. The storage devices of computers are also loosely known as *memory* systems, since the storage of such information resembles in some aspects the memory function of human beings.

Storage devices consist of punched cards, paper ribbon, electrostatic storage tubes, rotating magnetic drums, ferrite core matrices, magnetic tape reels, etc. Such devices are capable of storing a predetermined number of electric signals representing data or related information which can be converted into binary notation for computing purposes.

For practical purposes storage systems should be capable of

160

providing rapid access to the stored information—that is, the stored information should be available for quick read-out when needed. The storage device should also be capable of furnishing immediately the instructional information required for a particular mathematical calculation. Hence, most of the storage systems employed *within* the computer have a very rapid "information take-out" time (access time), although often storage devices with a lower rate access time are also employed *externally*. Such external memory systems consist of punched cards, punched paper tape, and magnetic tape reels.

COUNTER STORAGE

One storage device is the cascade flip-flop counter described earlier. In such a counter, a series of input pulses representing digits will be converted to a binary number by affecting the bistable condition of individual flip-flop circuits. For as long as power is applied to the counter, the latter will hold or maintain the number representing the series of pulses which were applied to the input. Hence, it "stores" such numbers for use as needed at some later time. When another train of pulses is applied, the bistable circuits again change (flip over), hence the second sequence of numbers is added to the first group which had been inserted, and the new number thus stored represents the *sum* of the two series of pulses which were applied.

By adding one number to another, the device "accumulates" the numbers by holding the sum of the numbers entered, and holds the last obtained sum in storage. As temporary storage devices during arithmetic operations, such counters (or storage registers as they are sometimes called) serve a vital function in computers.

The flip-flop circuit cascade counters can also be employed to act as storage devices for input pulses which represent binary numbers such as the one previously illustrated in Fig. 5-7, which accepted parallel pulse forms. A more complex type, accepting a serial binary train of numbers, is also used for storage purposes. This particular flip-flop is similar to the one shown in Fig. 5-6, except that the individual flip-flop circuits are not hooked up in cascade (where the output of one flip-flop circuit is applied to the cathode input of another flip-flop circuit). Instead, each flip-flop has an input which is procured from an and-circuit, and provisions are made for the insertion of a clearing pulse. The basic circuit for this system is shown in Fig. 6-1. Here the input is applied to the

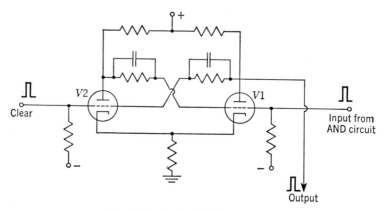

Fig. 6-1. Basic flip-flop storage.

grid of V1 as shown. The output is procured from the plate circuit of the first tube as shown earlier for the circuit in Fig. 5-6. Thus, the output pulse could consist of a positive polarity signal from the plate of V1 rather than the negative polarity obtained from the plate of V2 in cascade flip-flop counters.

A bank of such bistable flip-flop storage devices can be employed as shown in the block diagram of Fig. 6-2. Here delay lines are employed in conjunction with and-circuits (gates) and the flip-flop storage devices. The input to this storage system consists of a binary number fed to the input in sequential (serial train) order. Since the binary number is fed in sequential order, it cannot be applied to the flip-flop circuits directly since the sequence of pulses would upset the storage process. Instead, the sequence of pulses enters the delay lines and is also applied to the and-gates. Since, however, an and-gate must have a pulse applied to each input in order to have an output, no pulses arrive at the inputs to the flip-flop circuits initially. If, for instance, the binary number 101 is applied to the input, it will enter the delay lines. When the first digit of the input binary number reaches the output of the delay line

No. 3, the second-place binary digit and the third-place binary digit would be present at the output of the second and first delay lines, respectively. In the illustration employed, however, there would be

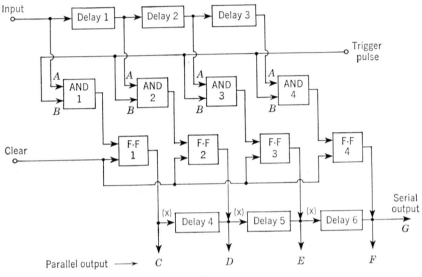

Fig. 6-2. Static storage.

no output from the second delay line since the second-place binary number is zero. At the time the first-place digit leaves the last delay line and is applied to the last and-gate, the other digits in the succeeding places of the binary number are also applied to the other and-gates as shown.

At this time a gating (triggering) pulse is applied to the line common to all the second (*B*) inputs of the and-gates. This gating pulse is timed to arrive at the instant when all the input pulses are present at all the and-gate *A* inputs, hence all and-circuits are gated simultaneously and thus permit the pulses from the delay lines to pass through to the storage flip-flop circuits. In the example given for Fig. 6-2 the output from the second delay line is zero; however, the output from its respective and-gate is also zero because the gating pulse alone is insufficient to open the circuit.

As soon as the gating pulse appears, the respective and-circuits open and the pulses thus applied to the grids of the flip-flop circuits as a parrallel train immediately alter the bistable state of the respective circuits, and thus register and store the number. Hence, the system becomes a static storage or static memory system and will retain this number for as long a period as power is applied to the system.

When the number which is stored in the static memory is needed, a clearing pulse is applied simultaneously to all the grids of the second tubes of the flip-flop circuits. (See Fig. 6-1.) This trigger pulse reverses the bistable condition of the tubes storing the digits and a positive pulse output will be obtained from such circuits. In the flip-flop circuits which register zero (V2 conducting at saturation) the application of a positive pulse to the grid of V2 will have no effect, since the tube is already conducting heavily. Hence, the bistable condition will not be reversed, and no output will be procured from that particular circuit.

When the clearing pulse is applied, the output from the static storage can be in the form of the entire number at one time (parallel form), or the binary sum can be obtained in serial form in the identical sequence in which the binary number was inserted originally.

For obtaining a parallel output, switches marked (x) in Fig. 6-2 are opened so that delay lines, Numbers 4, 5, and 6, are out of the circuit. A clearing pulse applied to the flip-flops will result in the binary number (in parallel form) appearing at output terminals C, D, E, and F.

In order to obtain the stored binary number in serial train form, the switches (x) in Fig. 6-2 are closed so that the delay lines are in the storage output circuit. The output is now obtainable from terminal G as shown in Fig. 6-2 when a clearing pulse is applied to the flip-flop circuits. As the flip-flop circuits are triggered by the clearing pulse, all that have numbers stored in them will produce an output. Thus, the output pulse from the last flip-flop circuit appears immediately at output terminal G. This is the first pulse to appear at the output, and hence represents the first-place digit of the stored number. The third flip-flop (if 101 were stored) has no stored pulse, hence there will be no output from this. The second flip-flop, however, has a stored pulse and the latter leaves the flip-flop circuit and enters delay line No. 5. At the output of delay line No. 5 the pulse is delayed by one place and enters delay line No. 6, at the output of which the pulse is delayed by an additional place and now appears in the third place. Hence, the output binary sum is 101 and coincides with the input binary sum.

The static storage system shown is capable of storing a four-place binary number, or the equivalent of zero through fifteen. For the storage of larger numbers, additional delays, and-gates, and flip-flops are necessary. For thorough familiarization of the manner in which the circuit functions, an additional analysis using a larger input number follows.

If the binary number 1111 is applied to the input, the first-place digit will arrive at the output of delay line No. 3 at the time that the last-place digit appears at the input of the first delay line and the first and-gate. At this time, the triggering pulse gates the and-circuits and hence all and-circuits open and the four pulses enter the flip-flop circuits. In consequence the second tube of each flip-flop circuit is driven to cut-off and the bistable state is changed to register the digit 1. Again, this number will be stored for as long a time as power is applied to the storage system.

When the output is required in parallel form, switches (x) to the delay lines are opened and the number 1111 appears at terminals C, D, E and F. If, however, the stored number is desired in serial train form, the switches are closed and the output derived from terminal G. The sequence of output occurs as follows: The first-place stored digit leaves the last flip-flop and appears at the output. At the same time, the stored digit from the third flip-flop enters delay line No. 6, is delayed by one pulse, and appears at the output as a second-place digit. Simultaneously with the outputs from the last two flip-flops, the second flip-flop delivers a pulse to delay line No. 5 and this pulse appears at the output as a third-place pulse. The output from the first flip-flop goes through three delay lines, and appears at the output as a fourth-place pulse. Again, the binary number (1111) appears at the output in sequential order in similar fashion to the manner in which it was originally applied to the input of the storage device.

If the number which is stored ends in 0, such as the binary number 110, it would seem that the read-out sum would be incorrect and appear as only 11, because the first place digit is 0. If the number is read out in parallel form and applied to an adder, drum storage device, or punched cards, etc., the 0 in first place would be retained. If applied to the flip-flop type counter, for instance (Fig. 5-7), the number 110 would still be the true number entered, because only the second and third stage flip-flops would be turned on. If the 110 is obtained from the storage register and placed in permanent storage on magnetic drums of the type described later, three drum tracks would be employed, with the first-place track not holding a digit 1, hence indicating the storage of 0. In punched cards, the area representing the first place would be left intact, and the second and third areas would be punched, the number again representing 110. For serial read-out, precise timing of the read-out start would be necessary to maintain the accuracy of the number.

SONIC STORAGE

As previously described, the static type of storage utilizes flip-flop circuits where the binary sum is registered by an "on" or "off" status of bistable devices. Other storage devices, however, are also utilized, including the magnetic tape types, ferrite cores, and sonic storage. The last is sometimes known as a *dynamic* storage device because it utilizes a delay and recirculation process. While the sonic type of storage is omitted in modern computers in favor of magnetic storage, sonic storage may still be encountered in older type computers, hence its basic operating principles are described herein.

The sonic delay line storage system converts the electric pulses into sonic (sound) pulses. By such a process, the high propagation velocity of the electric pulses is converted to a much lower propagation velocity by virtue of the electric pulses being converted to sonic impulses. The method in which this is done is shown in Fig. 6-3. The pulses are applied to a quartz crystal slab. A quartz crystal has a piezoelectric effect, and if the crystal slab is subjected to alternating pressure, stress, or strain it will generate electric signals. Conversely, if electric signals are applied to a crystal slab, it will convert such signals into sonic signals, since the crystal will vibrate when electric signals are applied to it. The piezoelectric effect of crystals is extensively employed in communications transmitters, where a slab of quartz crystal is made to vibrate at a high frequency and thus generate the basic carrier frequency of the transmitter. Crystals are also used in phonograph pickup cartridges where the movement of a needle (caused by record groove variations) subjects the crystal to varying stresses to produce sonic or audible sound vibrations.

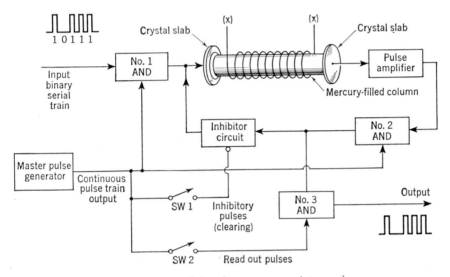

Fig. 6-3. Sonic delay line memory (storage).

In the sonic storage system shown in Fig. 6-3, the binary pulses which are applied to the first crystal slab are converted to sonic pulses because the crystal vibrates upon the application of the electric pulses. The first crystal slab is attached to a column of mercury. The mercury is in physical contact with one face of the first crystal slab and with one face of the second crystal slab, as shown. Hence, vibrations of the first crystal are transferred through the mercury and are applied to the face of the second crystal slab. The sonic vibrations on the second crystal slab set up electric pulses, hence the output from the second crystal slab consists of electric pulses having time interval spacings which coincide with the serial train applied to the first crystal slab. Because the propagation velocity through the mercury is much slower than the propagation velocity of the pulses through electric circuits, the serial train of pulses which had been applied to the first crystal slab has been delayed to a degree proportional to the length of the mercury column. If the mercury column produces the delay of 1 second, and pulses of $\frac{1}{2}$ microsecond duration are applied (with $\frac{1}{2}$ microsecond interval between them), it is obvious that a large number of binary digits can be accommodated at one time by the mercury column.

The electric pulses at the output of the second crystal are re-circulated through the system and fed back to the input of the first crystal slab. In this manner, the binary serial train is continuously changed from electric to sonic pulses and back to electric pulses, and recirculated for as long a period as power is applied to the storage circuits.

The conversion process of electric pulses to sonic pulses and back to electric pulses, plus the effect on the sonic pulses by the mercury column, has an adverse effect on the waveshape and amplitude of the rectangular pulses of the binary serial train. Hence, the output pulses from the second crystal slab are distorted in shape and attenuated with respect to their amplitude. If such distorted and low amplitude pulses are now recirculated through the mercury column, they will reappear at the output of the second crystal slab with even greater distortion and lower amplitude. Continuous re-circulation would eventually obliterate the pulses entirely. To prevent loss of such pulses, it is necessary to include provisions in the sonic delay storage to assure recirculation of pulses having good amplitude and proper waveshape. This is done by utilizing and-circuits which have the ability to substitute new pulses for the distorted pulses.

As mentioned earlier, an and-circuit will have an output only if a pulse is applied to each input simultaneously. Such being the case, the circuit can be utilized to substitute new pulses for the old distorted ones. This is done by applying a continuous train of pulses to one of the inputs of the and-circuit from the master pulse generator. Since the pulses derived from the master pulse generator are undistorted in shape, they are used to replace the distorted pulses which are circulating in the memory system. The pulses circulating in the memory system, however, represent a binary serial train, and may have space intervals between pulses which represent binary zeros. Hence, the undistorted pulses derived from the master pulse generator must be gated into the storage system at proper time intervals to coincide with the pulses representing the binary serial train. The and-circuit will gate the master pulses in the proper time intervals to coincide with the binary pulse intervals, as well as zero intervals. When the master generator pulses are applied to an and-circuit, there will be no output except when the original (and distorted) pulses also arrive at the other input to the and-circuit. When simultaneous input pulses are present, the master generator pulses appear at the output. In this manner, the distorted pulses are replaced by undistorted pulses from the master pulse generator. This method for using an and-gate circuit for converting distorted binary number pulses to ones having undistorted waveshapes is not, of course, confined to sonic storage devices. The same procedures can be used for restoring pulse shapes at any place where pulse distortion is present.

The binary serial train pulses which are to be stored may also be distorted because of their transit through the main computer circuits. Hence, the input binary serial train is immediately applied to an and-circuit (No. 1 in Fig. 6-3) and replaced by pulses from the master pulse generator. As shown, the master pulse generator supplies a continuous train of pulses to one of the inputs of the first and-circuit, and such pulses are gated into the mercury delay line by the binary serial train applied to the other input of the first and-circuit. Thus, undistorted pulses are applied to the first crystal slab. If such pulses are of low amplitude, a pulse amplifier may also be employed between the first and-circuit and the first crystal slab.

In the recirculation process, the binary train of pulses is applied to one of the inputs of an inhibitory and-circuit. For as long as switch No. 1 is open, no pulses will be applied to the inhibitory input of the and-circuit, hence the serial train appears at the output of the inhibitory circuit and is applied to the first crystal slab of the sonic delay line.

There are occasions when a serial train may be stored in the sonic delay line memory, and it is later discovered that the number so stored is no longer needed. When this is the case, the circulating serial train can be obliterated or cleared by closing switch No. 1. When the latter switch is closed, a continuous train of pulses is applied to the inhibitory and-circuit, and this train of pulses will inhibit or suppress the train of pulses arriving from the second and-circuit. Thus, the recirculation of the binary serial train is stopped and the memory cleared of the stored binary sum.

If the information which has been stored is required at any particular time, it can be obtained from the output line of the third and-circuit. As shown in Fig. 6-3, the output from the second and-circuit not only feeds the inhibitory and-circuit but also the third and-circuit. There will be no output from the third and-circuit, however, unless pulses are also applied to the other input of the third and-circuit. Hence, to obtain an output of the binary serial train which is recirculating, switch No. 2 must be closed so that pulses from the master pulse generator are applied to the third and-circuit in order to gate the latter. The output from the third and-circuit will then consist of undistorted pulses selected from the master generator pulses by the binary serial train pulses from the second and-circuit.

Provisions must be incorporated into the sonic delay memory so that the third and-circuit has an open gate condition which starts at the first binary digit of the serial train which is recirculating. This is necessary to assure that the output serial train starts at the proper initial digit.

Since the velocity of sonic waves in any medium will vary in proportion to the temperature of that medium, it is essential that the mercury column in the sonic delay line memory system be maintained carefully at a constant temperature. One method for doing this is to utilize a heating coil as shown in Fig. 6-3. The terminals marked (x) are furnished power which is carefully controlled with respect to voltage variations so that the heat generated by the coil is held constant, and thus the temperature of the mercury is maintained at the same level during the storage process.

The velocity of sonic pulses through mercury is approximately 5.7×10^4 inches per second. Thus, if the mercury column is 10 inches long, it will take 175.4 microseconds for one pulse to travel the length of the column as indicated by the following formula:

$$\frac{10}{5.7 \times 10^4} = 0.0001754 \text{ or } 175.4 \text{ microseconds}$$

Since modern computers often use pulses with a fraction of a microsecond duration, over 500 binary digits can be stored in a 10-inch mercury column and over 1,000 binary digits in a 20-inch mercury column. However, as the column length is increased in order to store larger numbers, temperature stability of the mercury becomes more difficult to achieve. Long mercury columns increase signal travel time through the storage device, hence information would not be available with so rapid an access time as in the shorter mercury columns. Hence, the mercury delay lines are utilized in lengths which are capable of storing only a few thousand binary digits. Since, however, 1,000 or 2,000 binary digits would represent a large decimal number, the shorter length columns are quite suitable for most of the storage problems encountered in digital computers. On occasions where rapid access time to high numerical value stored numbers is necessary, several mercury column storage systems have been employed simultaneously in a parallel hookup to increase the number of binary digits which can be stored. The mercury memory of SEAC (Standards Eastern Automatic Computer) built in 1950 contained sixty-four mercury filled acoustic lines.

MAGNETIC STORAGE

Digital computers also employ magnetic tape for storage purposes. The principle involved is similar to that used in tape recorders in the home and in broadcasting stations. In tape recorders for the home, tape reels up to 7 inches in diameter are employed, containing approximately 1,200 feet of plastic tape of the cellulose acetate or polyester type. For home recorders the tape is approximately $\frac{1}{4}$ inch wide and is utilized at $3\frac{1}{4}$ inches per second, $7\frac{1}{2}$ inches per second, or 15 inches per second.

The plastic tape has one side coated with a magnetic material combining a red oxide with a binder. The oxide, like iron or steel, can be magnetized by subjecting it to a magnetic field. Once magnetized, it retains such magnetism for an indefinite period, and can thus store information imparted to it in the form of varying magnetic densities.

During the storage process, the side coated with the oxide is passed over a recording head in a manner such as shown in Fig. 6-4. The recording head consists of a laminated core and a coil, and

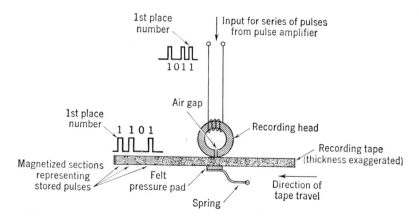

Fig. 6-4. Magnetic recording storage.

when pulses or other types of signals are applied to the input leads of the coil, a magnetic field is generated across the very small air gap. As the tape passes over this air gap, the alternating magnetic field will change the molecular structure of the oxide material and magnetize sections of it in accordance with the intensity and polarity of the fields generated across the air gap of the recording head. When it is necessary to procure the stored information from the tape, it is again run over a recording head (now called a playback head), and the varying degrees of magnetism along the tape will now induce a voltage in the pickup coil. The output leads from the coil will then contain the pulses or other signal information which were originally placed on the tape when the tape was run through initially. Some recorders utilize one head both as a recording head and a playback head, while others have separate heads for recording and playback. A felt pad, mounted on a spring, applies tension to the uncoated side of the tape and maintains a constant pressure of the tape against the recording head during either playback or erase.

The illustration in Fig. 6-4 is simplified and does not show the amplifiers necessary to bring the signal information up to the level required for placement on the recording head. The amplifiers, however, are roughly similar to audio amplifiers found in radios and phonographs. For tape recorders used for voice and music, recording and playback make it necessary to employ a supersonic bias (usually above 50,000 cycles). Such supersonic bias permits operation of the recording on a more linear portion of the hysteresis loop of the magnetic recording curve and provides a minimum of distortion and a maximum of linearity. Linearity of recording in digital computer magnetic storage is not a factor, however, because the stored information *saturates* the tape and no bias is required.

The range of frequencies which can be recorded on tape depends to a large degree on how narrow the recording head gap is, the speed of the tape, and how accurately the tape head is set in the machine. The narrow gap must be placed as close as possible to a true vertical plane to permit full realization of its advantages. A slight variation from the vertical will nullify the effects of a narrow gap, since the magnetic field will have a much wider equivalent effect on the tape as the latter rides. This is shown at (A) and (B) of Fig. 6-5. At (A) a narrow gap is shown in a true vertical position,

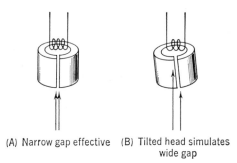

(A) Narrow gap effective   (B) Tilted head simulates
                                 wide gap

Fig. 6-5. Results of tilt on effective gap width.

and the effective width is equivalent to the true width. At (B), however, an exaggerated tilt of the head is shown, and in effect the gap width is greater than would be the case without tilt. Thus, for good high frequency reproduction it is necessary to have a very narrow width and as perfect a perpendicular setting as possible.

The range of frequencies is dependent on the speed because the faster the tape rides past the narrow gap, the higher the frequency that can be recorded. Since a narrow gap shortens the width of the magnetic density of a given bit of stored information, it also follows that a faster tape speed will spread such signal information out over a larger tape surface area than would be the case with a lower tape speed. If the tape speed is too slow, the rapid alternations of signal energy may occur before the tape has made sufficient movement to spread such information out. In consequence, the negative and positive changes of magnetic intensity will overlap on the tape and prevent the recording of it.

In home and professional recorders, tape speeds of 15 inches per second were initially required in order to procure a fidelity of recording up to approximately 15,000 cycles per second. Later developments in tape heads, however, permitted the recording of frequencies up to 15,000 cycles with tape speeds of only $7\frac{1}{2}$ inches per second. The lower tape speeds for higher recording frequencies are desirable since there is a considerable saving in tape footage.

For the recording and storage of digital pulses, frequency response is related to the duration and rise time of the pulses employed. When a pulse which causes a loss of some of the high frequency components is stored in the device, the pulse will be distorted since the sharp leading edge and the abrupt change from vertical to horizontal will be lost because of the loss of high frequency components.

Pulses applied to the recording head are usually in a serial train of digits representing the number. Referring back to the illustration for the recording head in Fig. 6-4, if the binary number 1011 (decimal number eleven) were to be stored, the first place binary digit would be applied to the recording head initially and it would leave a section of the tape magnetized. The next place binary digit would enter the recording head after the tape area which stored the initial digit has moved away. Thus, the second place digit would be stored. The tape would then move past the head for a longer interval without any pulse going in, representing the zero of the binary train. The fourth place digit would then enter the recording head and magnetize a section of the tape. Thus, the left-hand section of the tape would have stored the first place digit and the right-

Fig. 6-6. Tape transport detail of Elecom.
(Courtesy of Underwood Corp.)

hand section of the magnetized area of the tape the fourth place digit. If this were then run through a similar head for playback, the direction of the tape past the head would be similar to the direction initially used and hence the output from the tape would again be the binary number 1011.

Fig. 6-6 illustrates the recording head mechanism and tape transport section used in the Elecom digital computer, manufactured by the Underwood Corporation. In systems of this type the take-up reel exerts a slight pull on the tape, while the other reel must exert a slight drag to prevent the tape from running loosely. Pressure rollers, actuated from the motor, keep the tape going past the head at constant speed.

Instead of tape, some magnetic storage devices utilize a large cylindical drum coated with the oxide magnetic material. The drum is rotated at high speeds (given later for typical units) and information is stored in narrow tracks along the circumference. A series of recording heads is placed so that they span the width of the drum. The recording heads can then impart to the drum a considerable store of information.

Fig. 6-7 shows the basic principle of the magnetic drum type of storage. The drum rotor is mounted on a shaft; a motor comprises part of the system and is attached directly to the drum shaft. Heads are placed in horizontal rows on an enclosing casing as more clearly illustrated in Fig. 6-8. This illustrates the Model 1100 magnetic storage drum manufactured by Remington Rand Univac, Division of Sperry Rand Corporation. This drum has 224 tracks, with each track accommodating approximately 2,100 binary digits (bits). Thus, the drum has a capacity for storing 470,400 bits. The drum diameter is 8.5 inches with a usable length of approximately 14.5 inches. Approximately eighty binary digits are stored in one circumferential inch with a maximum access time of 17 milliseconds. The nominal revolutions per minute are 3,510. The motor develops $\frac{1}{3}$ horsepower at this speed, and the approximate weight of the unit is 125 pounds.

A larger unit is the Model 1107 shown in Fig. 6-9, also manufactured by Remington Rand Univac. This has 175 tracks, with a storage capacity per track of approximately 4,190 binary digits. The greater storage capacity is available because the drum diameter is 17 inches as compared to 8.5 inches for the previously described drum. Hence, the Model 1107 has a maximum binary digit storage capacity of 733,250. Maximum access time is 34 milliseconds, and the usable length of the drum is approximately 11 inches. Nominal revolutions per minute for the drum are 1,740, and a $\frac{3}{4}$ horsepower

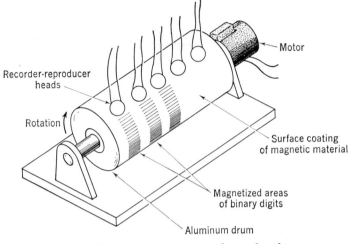

Recorder-reproducer heads

Rotation

Motor

Surface coating of magnetic material

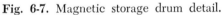

Magnetized areas of binary digits

Aluminum drum

Fig. 6-7. Magnetic storage drum detail.

Fig. 6-8. Model 1100 magnetic storage drum of Remington Rand Univac.

motor is utilized. This storage drum weighs approximately 270 pounds.

As shown in Fig. 6-8, plug-in heads and cables are utilized so that any number of the available head positions can be employed as required. The recording-read-out heads are Model 202, available from the above manufacturer. The core material of the head is

Fig. 6-9. Model 1107 drum of Remington Rand Univac.

ferrite, with a coil winding of approximately 10 microhenry inductance. Nominal recording pulse duration is 1.5 microseconds, and nominal head drum spacing is 0.002 inch.

Magnetic storage drums come in various sizes other than the ones mentioned in the foregoing paragraphs. Some drums have a diameter of less than 5 inches, and others have a diameter which exceeds 20 inches. The larger drums use a motor with a horsepower rating as high as $1\frac{1}{2}$, while the smaller drums use a correspondingly lower horsepower rating, often as low as $\frac{1}{5}$. Some of the smaller units weigh less than 50 pounds while the larger ones weigh well over 500 pounds. Some types, such as the Univac Models 1119 and 1120, have a drum motor driven by power from a motor-alternator supplying variable frequency and voltage, which permits rotating the drum at speeds between 4,800 rpm and 12,000 rpm.

As with any magnetic recording, the information recorded on a drum can be altered as required. Any bit of information on the magnetic drum can be erased and replaced by new information in a matter of a few milliseconds. With appropriate associated circuitry, information which is stored on a drum can be exchanged or channeled to input and output devices such as electric typewriters, punched cards, punched tapes, high speed printers, etc., as more fully described in the next chapter.

As mentioned earlier, magnetic recording has the advantage that power failure cannot cause a loss of the stored information, and the magnetized areas of the drum (or tape) can be stored for a long time without information loss or appreciable deterioration of the signal amplitude as identified by the intensity of the magnetized area.

In drum storage systems several tracks (usually the first three tracks) are used as so-called *control tracks* or *clock tracks* for synchronization purposes during read-in and read-out. Obviously, when a group of binary *bits* (digits) are recorded on a rapidly moving drum some means must be provided so that during read-out the bit recorded first is read-out first. Otherwise, at the start of read-out the drum may be in such a position that the read-out starts at the middle or toward the end of the group of binary bits which were recorded. For accurate timing purposes the control tracks have recorded on them permanent magnetized sectors which provide for the positive locating of a specific digit or word (a word is a unit group of binary bits). The magnetized sectors usually include: pulses used for identification of the drum area where a word group starts, pulses for timing purposes, digit pulses for identifying word separation, and pulses for locating specific digit positions or groups of digits. Thus, to read-out a particular word or word sequence, information must be supplied to the circuits associated with the drum, such information specifying the particular track in which the stored data is retained, as well as the sector in which the data is located with respect to the identifying origin pulse. Such read-out information must be supplied the computer as part of the instructions making up what is known as a *program*, as discussed in the next chapter.

FERRITE MEMORY

Another method for storage used in digital computers consists of using small magnetic rings composed of ferrite. Ferrite is a very hard and brittle material composed of spinel crystals consisting of a mixture of magnetic metals such as nickel, manganese, and zinc. Ferrite rods have been used extensively in portable radios as the core of the built-in antenna. Such rods have an extremely high Q obtained because of the high permeability of the material. For computer use, the ferrite material is formed into tiny rings, and they are sometimes referred to as ferrite toroids or ferrite memory cores. Core sizes vary, some smaller ones having an outside diameter of only 0.08 inch and an inside diameter of 0.05 inch. Larger ones range up to 0.4 inch outside diameter, and 0.2 inch inside diameter. The thickness ranges between about 0.025 inch for the smaller sizes, to 0.125 inch for the larger.

The magnetic properties of the ferrite rings are such that they retain stored information without undue disturbance from other low voltage signals which may be applied when the computer is in operation, as more fully detailed later. When an energizing current of sufficient amplitude is employed, the ferrite cores become magnetized with a polarity which coincides with that of the energizing polarity. The magnetic field which is created (positive polarity, for instance) will be retained until a current of opposite polarity is applied to the core.

When it is necesary to store information, a particular pulse of energy will magnetize the core along a nearly rectangular hysteresis loop. Figure 6-10 illustrates the hysteresis loop of ferrite as represented by the solid lines, compared to ordinary magnetic material shown by the dashed lines. Note that the ferrite hysteresis loop almost represents a rectangle in comparison to the curved type of loop for the ordinary magnetic material.

The vertical axis represents flux density (symbol B) and the horizontal axis represents the magnetizing force (symbol H). Such a graph is called a B-H curve of magnetic characteristics. The unit of flux density or magnetism is known as *gauss*, while the unit for the magnetizing force is *oersted*. The relationship between the two is that a magnetizing force of one oersted produces a flux density of one gauss. (One gauss represents one magnetic line per square centimeter of cross sectional area in air.)

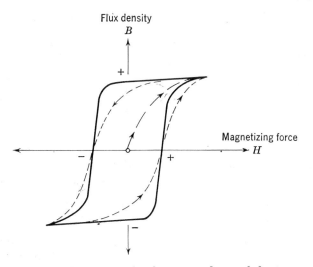

Fig. 6-10. Nearly rectangular hysteresis loop of ferrite toroid (solid lines) vs. ordinary magnetic material.

The *B-H* curve is procured by increasing the magnetizing force on the magnetic material, and noting the increase in flux density. Magnetizing force to soft iron (etc.) can be applied by forming a loop of wire around the iron and running current through the wire. The wire itself forms a field composed of magnetic lines of force which act to energize the soft iron. If the current is increased, the magnetism in the iron will also become stronger until the leveling off portion as shown in the graph. The rise in flux density for ordinary material curves upward from the center zero line and tapers off to the right as shown by the dotted lines. In reducing the magnetizing force the curve fails to retrace the curve back on the forward trace line to the zero point, but curves back down at the left as shown by the arrows in the dotted section. Thus, when the magnetizing force is zero, the flux density is still quite high (known as *residual* magnetism or a remnant magnetism). Thus, the flux density *B* lags behind the magnetizing force *H*. This lag phenomenon is known as *hysteresis*, hence the graph of the curve is called a hysteresis loop. With a reversing polarity, the curve drops down to the left below the zero line as shown. Decreasing the magnetizing force causes the right-hand trace upward, again failing to intercept the zero line. The entire magnetic material would have to be thoroughly demagnetized to be able to start at zero again and trace upward.

Because the ferrite magnetic cores have a rectangular hysteresis loop, the ferrite core is inherently a bistable element. An inspection of Fig. 6-10, which shows the rectangular loop, will indicate that the magnetic induction of the core can be equivalent to a charge in the plus direction or a charge in the minus direction, depending on the polarity of the magnetizing field current. For the purpose of computer usage, when the magnetic field is in the positive direction it is assigned either 0 or 1, with the negative direction being assigned the opposite designation. For instance, when in the plus direction it can represent 0, and when in the minus direction it can represent the binary digit 1. Hence, when the core is magnetized in the negative direction it would store the digit 1 and this direction would be the *write* direction. When the core is now magnetized in the positive direction, the information can be read out, hence the positive direction can be considered the *read* direction. If the core is magnetized in the so-called negative direction, it can be switched to the positive direction by the application of a read pulse which has full amplitude. During the change from the negative condition to the read-out condition, a voltage is induced in the sense wire (described later) which runs through the center of the core. On the other hand, if the core is in the zero state (positive), the application of a read pulse will produce very little voltage in the sense (output) winding. Hence, the ferrite core, because of its rectangular hysteresis loop, has the ability to select or discriminate between two conditions or states. For this reason it is particularly adaptable with respect to binary arithmetic where only 0 and 1 are utilized.

For digital computer storage use the cores are assembled on a flat panel and connected together by cross-wiring to form what is known as a matrix, in similar fashion to the enlarged section of a typical unit illustrated in Fig. 6-11. Independent and insulated wires are run through the cores as shown, with the vertical series marked *A*, *B*, etc. intercepting at the core a series of horizontal wires marked *N*, *O*, etc. in the illustration. Thus, each individual ferrite core has one pair of wires at intersection. Voltage applied to any

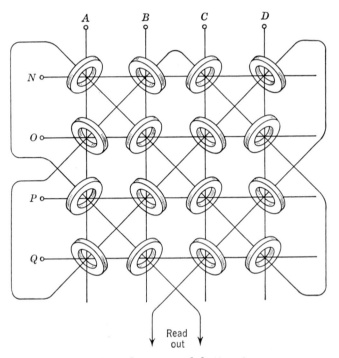

Fig. 6-11. Enlarged section of ferrite ring memory.

horizontal or vertical line will cause current to flow in that wire and hence a magnetic field is set up around the wire. The magnetic field created by the one wire is only about one-half the amplitude required to shift the magnetic field of the core. When the other intersecting wire of that core is energized, however, the combining fields are sufficiently high to change the magnetic state of the core where the two lines intersect. Thus, if the current is made to flow through the wire marked *B*, a field will be set up along this wire, but it will be of insufficient amplitude to magnetize the four cores in the vertical row. If a current is now applied to the horizontal line marked *N*, the two magnetic fields established at the intersection of *N* and *B* will be greater than the coercive force of the core and hence sufficient to magnetize that particular ferrite core. The core will now resist any change of the magnetic polarity it acquired until a magnetic field of opposite polarity is applied to the two lines which intersect at the core of this ring.

When a reverse polarity voltage is applied at the intersection, the ferrite core again changes its flux polarity and is switched from one state to another. This shift in its magnetic state creates a changing magnetic flux field which induces a voltage into the wire intersecting the core at an angle. As shown in Fig. 6-11, this is a continuous winding the ends of which terminate at the bottom and are designated as *read-out*. Thus, the voltage induced in the read-out wire represents the stored bit of binary information which had been retained by a particular ferrite core ring. The output bit, ranging in amplitude between 50 and 75 millivolts, is amplified to the required degree and channeled to the necessary circuits of the computer to be processed as required. The read-out line is sometimes referred to as a "sense" wire because it is used to sense or ascertain the read-out pulse. On read-out the stored information is, of course, lost. If the stored information is to be retained after read-out, the information must be recirculated and reapplied to the core to regenerate it again.

The matrix shown in Fig. 6-11 consists of only sixteen ferrite rings, though any particular matrix may have well over 225 cores, depending on requirements and the manufacturer. Each matrix, however, will be wired in a fashion similar to that illustrated in Fig. 6-11. (Matrix factors are discussed more fully in the next chapter.) Switching time ranges from 1 microsecond to 5 microseconds, depending on the type and quality of the ferrite core. Driving current ranges from 400 to 800 milliamperes.

A complete ferrite storage system may have from a few to nearly fifty *matrices*. With fifty matrices and 225 cores, it is possible to store 11,250 binary bits. The read-out line or sense winding intersects *all* the cores of one matrix no matter how many are employed in any particular matrix. The letter designations shown are, of course, for reference purposes only and may be designated by some other symbol or number, depending on the particular choice utilized by a particular manufacturer. The intersecting wires which cross at the core are, as mentioned earlier, insulated and do not form a physical electrical contact.

A typical commercial ferrite core matrix frame is illustrated in Fig. 6-12. This unit is manufactured by General Ceramics Corporation. The frames are available in several sizes from 4.5 inches square to 7 inches square, some containing 100 cores, and others having 256 cores, 1,024 cores, and 4,096 cores.

Fig. 6-12. Ferrite core matrix frame.
(Courtesy of General Ceramics Corp.)

ELECTROSTATIC STORAGE

Another method for storage is the use of a cathode ray tube, imparting the information to be stored to the phosphor screen. Ordinary cathode ray tubes such as used in oscilloscopes can be employed, though better results are obtained by using tubes especially designed for storage purposes. Typical tubes in use are the 3KP1 and the 5UP1. The former has a 3-inch screen and the latter a 5-

inch screen. Both tubes have a green phosphor with medium persistence. (Television tubes also have a medium persistence, but generally use a white phosphor.)

Williams and Kilburn originated the system of electrostatic storage, and the cathode ray tube used for storage is sometimes referred to as the "Williams' tube." Information stored on the phosphor screen is in the form of dots and dashes, the dot representing a binary 0 and the dash representing a binary 1. The control grid of the tube receives the signal information consisting of binary-number pulses, and as with normal vacuum tubes, the control grid is influential in regulating the amount of current from the cathode. The grid is held at cut-off during the absence of pulses, and when information is to be stored, each pulse applied to the control grid releases electrons from the cathode. The electron "gun" within the cathode ray tube accelerates the beam current and also focuses the electron beam into a sharp beam which strikes the phosphor coating of the cathode ray tube. When the beam strikes the phosphor with high velocity, electrons are knocked off the area (secondary emission) leaving a positively charged area on the phosphor.

The beam, in addition to being turned on and off, must also be deflected across the face of the tube in order to distribute the dot and dash information. Also, the beam must be pulled down the screen periodically as new lines of information are recorded. A gradual horizontal deflection of an electron beam is accomplished by a sawtooth voltage applied to the horizontal deflection plates. The rising voltage on the deflection plates causes a gradual shift of the beam from left to right. For causing the beam position to shift from one horizontal line to another in steps, a "staircase" type voltage must be applied to the vertical deflection plates. A staircase or "stepped" voltage is one which rises sharply, then remains at that level for a short interval, rises again by a predetermined amount, and again remains at the new level for a short interval, etc.

In the Williams' tube, the electron beam sets up an electron distribution on the screen which conforms to the information stored. A plate made of conductive material is fastened to the outside face of the tube for the purposes of detecting the stored information. If the stored information is to be seen for inspectional purposes, the plate may be made of glass manufactured by inclusion of conductive material. Information which is stored on the phosphor in terms of positively charged areas forms a capacitance between the phosphor plus area and the conducting external plate. The glass faceplate acts as the capacitor dielectric. The stored information is obtained from the tube by scanning the phosphor with an uninterrupted electron beam. The scanning beam, when encountering a section where information is stored, replenishes the missing electrons and hence affects the capacitance area. This process will cause a current flow (by capacitance coupling) in the pickup plate. The signal energy, however, is extremely weak and requires considerable amplification. Read-out time can be as short as 10 microseconds, and storage capacity for a single tube is approximately 1,000 bits.

The Williams' tube can be used either for serial mode storage or for parallel mode. For serial mode, the binary number representations are stored in sequence along horizontal sections of the screen, and read out in sequential order as needed. For parallel storage, a number of cathode ray tubes must be employed, the required number dictated by the number of binary digits in the information to be stored. For both read-in and read-out all the electron beams must be aimed at the proper section of the phosphor screen. With parallel operation the access (read-out) time is shortened considerably. The digital computer SEAC (Standards Eastern Automatic Computer) developed by the National Bureau of Standards was originally designed for forty-eight electrostatic storage tubes, of which forty-five were employed at any one time for parallel mode operation.

Stored information tends to leak off the screen surface, hence the information must be regenerated by recirculating the stored data. Sweep timing must be maintained accurately during the restoration process to prevent smudging of the information, and sweep timing must also be accurate for proper read-out. Because of these and other critical operational factors, the electrostatic storage type of memory has not been so popular as the magnetic memory types.

Figure 6-13 shows a typical electrostatic storage system. Synchronizing circuits are utilized to stabilize the sweep signals, and the synchronizing circuits also hold the regeneration system in proper timing relationships. The information to be stored is applied to the input as shown, and the circuits therein also provide the signals available at the read-out terminal.

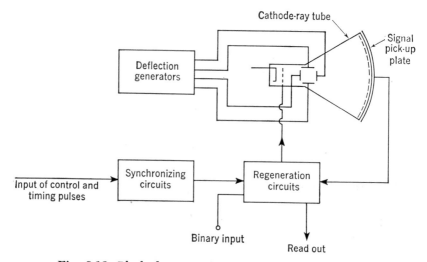

Fig. 6-13. Block diagram of electrostatic storage system.

Questions Relating to Chapter 6

1. Briefly explain what is meant by the storage system of a digital computer.

2. Explain how a cascaded flip-flop counter system can be used as a storage device.

3. *a*) Draw a block diagram of a sonic storage system.
   b) Label each block to denote the type of circuit employed.
   c) How is the high propagation velocity of the electric pulses converted to low propagation velocity of sonic pulses?

4. Explain how and-gates can be used to correct pulse distortion.

5. *a*) Explain the advantages of magnetic tape and drum storage over the sonic storage system.
   b) How does a magnetic storage device retain information?

6. *a*) What are the general drum diameters used in magnetic storage?
   b) At what speeds do the drums rotate?

7. Briefly explain the principles involved in ferrite storage.

8. How does the hysteresis loop of the ferrite core differ from that of ordinary magnetic material? What is the advantage of such a hysteresis loop?

9. How can information be obtained from the ferrite storage device and still leave the information in storage?

10. Explain the general principles involved in electrostatic storage systems.

7

□ □ □
□ □ □
■ □ □

Programming

The digital computer can solve a variety of problems, ranging from simple to the highly complex. The computer, however, cannot think for itself, and it must be told how to handle the particular problems which it must solve. If a particularly complex equation is to be solved, the machine must be fed information regarding the step-by-step procedures which it must undertake in order to arrive at a solution. The list of instructions involving the particular steps for solving an equation is called a *routine* or a *program.* The term program is usually applied to a set of instructions or routines, and a program can be thought of as a sequential-step plan for the solution of a problem, without it being a solution in itself.

Programming for a computer is similar to the programming which would be undertaken for solving a particular problem with an ordinary desk computer. If 328 is to be multiplied by 45 and the product divided by 8, for instance, the number 328 would be applied to the desk computer by depressing the appropriate keys. Once the number 328 has thus been entered into the computer, the computer has literally *stored* the information and is ready to utilize this number in accordance with the directions which are to be given subsequently. When the multiplier numbers are entered and the multiplication key depressed, the machine is ready to give the product when the "answer" key is depressed. Thus, for the simple example given, the keys of the machine were depressed in accordance with a program of instructions which fits the particular mechanism of the computer.

In similar manner, a program must be set out for digital computers to solve a particular problem or equation. Some commercial computers can be programmed quite easily and require only a little experience by new personnel. Other computers, however, require trained personnel for programming complex equations. While the sequence of operations for a particular equation may not change, the methods by which the program is applied to various computers differ considerably. An operator must refer to the instruction sheets which accompany a particular computer in order to learn the proper procedures utilized in programming.

Programming not only involves the setting up of the equation in its particular sequence, but also translating the sequence of steps into the sequence of instructions which can be fed to the machine. The routine can be applied to a computer by depressing appropriate switches or typewriter keys, or by using punched cards or magnetic tape. Each instruction received by the computer will close appropriate circuits to carry on the calculation. The circuits may be closed by solenoid relays, by mercury switch relays, or by gating and switching tubes. Once the proper relays have been closed, the calculation circuits of the computer complete the entire sequence of steps in a much shorter interval than would be required by a staff of mathematicians.

A particular program may involve only a few minutes of preparation, or, in case of extremely complex calculations, it may take several days, weeks, or even months for its preparation. Similarly, the answer (read-out) from a computer may take only a few seconds, or several hours, or much longer, depending on the complexity of the problem.

SWITCHING SYSTEMS

A relay is illustrated in Fig. 7-1, and consists of a coil with an iron core (solenoid) which becomes an electromagnet when current flows through the coil. The magnetic pull of the fields of the electromagnet attracts a flexible reed, and when the reed is pulled downward it closes a switch. The switch can consist of a simple

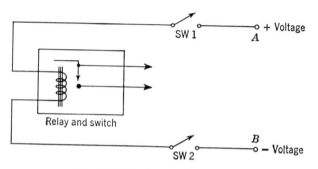

Fig. 7-1. Single switching unit.

single-pole single-throw type, or a more complex type of switch such as double-pole double-throw, etc. When no voltage is applied to the coil, the switch is in its open position. When a voltage is applied, however, the switch closes and then can interconnect a multiplier and a storage system, a subtracter and an adder, or do any other switching required.

In order to obtain increased flexibility with the least number of controls, the relays are hooked up as shown in Fig. 7-1. Here, a line designated as A has applied to it the plus polarity voltage, while the line indicated B is the minus voltage feed line. Two switches are shown for closing the A and B lines, switch No.1 and switch No. 2. If only switch No. 1 is closed, the open circuit for the minus voltage will prevent the relay from being closed. When switch No. 2 is closed, but switch No. 1 open, the relay is still not in operation. Only when both switches are closed will the relay be in operation. Thus, the two switches are similar to the and-circuits previously discussed, where neither one alone is effective. In this instance the closing of two switches is necessary for working the relay and it would appear that the circuit could be simplified by utilizing only one switch. Actually, however, the particular arrangement used becomes more simple than other systems when applied to a number of relays. This is shown in Fig. 7-2, where four relays are utilized and four switches are shown for closing the circuits. Thus, in the previous example two switches were required to close one relay, while here combinations of only four switches will actuate four relays.

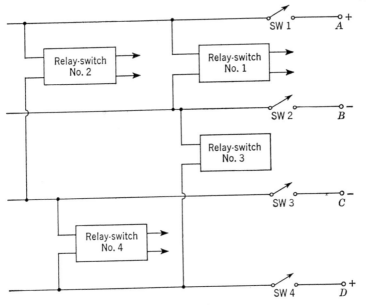

Fig. 7-2. Circuit for four relay switches.

A simplified schematic of this arrangement is shown in Fig. 7-3 which indicates the four relays and the particular switches which must be closed to actuate them. Closing switch A and switch B will influence relay No. 1 but will not affect the others. Number 3 relay is not affected because it requires a plus voltage from the D switch which in this instance is not closed. Relay No. 2 will not function even though the A switch is depressed because the C switch is open and hence does not apply the missing negative potential.

As the system is made more elaborate, fewer switches are required to control a given number of relays. Sixteen relays used in the foregoing pattern, for instance, require only eight switches. Hence, while the number of switches which have to be depressed is still two switches for each relay, the use of similar switches in combination with others reduces the number of switches required. Thus, many functions can be obtained by utilizing this type of circuit. This circuit is sometimes referred to as a *matrix* since its circuit diagram resembles a matrix. The term "matrix" for circuit arrangement of switches, relays, resistors, or other components in a rectangular form originated with the mathematician James J. Syl-

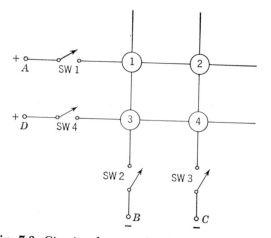

Fig. 7-3. Circuit schematic for four relay switches.

vester (1850), who so designated an array of numbers in rectangular form and indicated a special calculation method which can be performed therefrom. In using the matrix principle, many functions can be obtained from a single typewriter keyboard, or a small card in which holes are punched to conform to the switches which are to be actuated.

With a complete alphabet, A to Z, 26 letters take care of 169 relays by using letters in various combinations. The complete matrix for the full alphabet is shown in Fig. 7-4. Depressing the switch in the A line applies a plus voltage to relays No. 1 through No. 13, but none of these will operate as long as the minus voltage is missing. Depressing keys A and Q, for instance, will actuate relay No. 4, since the A applies a plus voltage to this relay. The minus voltages also applied to relays No. 17, No. 30, No. 43, etc. are ineffective since no plus potentials are applied to these.

For illustrating the *address* system used in computers, a few of the relay switches associated with Fig. 7-4 have been detailed in Fig. 7-5. Here, a storage device is shown, as well as a multiplier. Other units could, of course, be employed for these particular re-

lay switches, but the ones illustrated were chosen to indicate a
simple form of address.

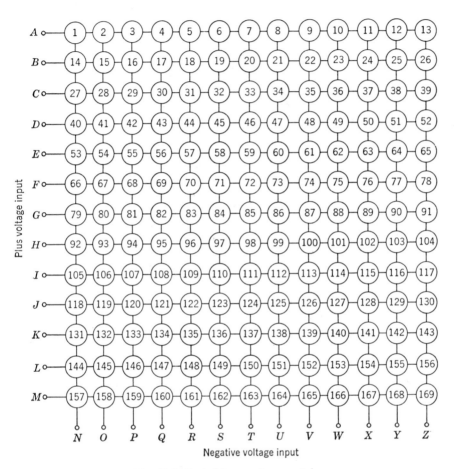

Fig. 7-4. Switching system matrix.

Since an address specifies a location of something (a storage location or a relay, for instance) the matrix arrangement provides a
number of address locations. In programming, the operation part
of the instruction or routine tells what is to be done. An address in
a particular routine might, for instance, consist of ER with respect
to Fig. 7-5. The selection of this address and applying voltage to
the E and R terminals means that this address involves the selection
of relay No. 57 which connects the X terminal to the storage for

whatever purpose is required. Hence, any information applied to the X terminal will be placed into the storage unit.

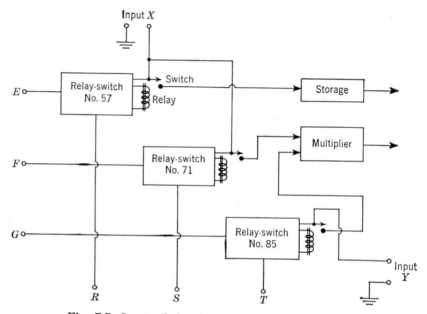

Fig. 7-5. Sectional detail No. 1 of switching system.

An address of FS means the selection of relay No. 71 which connects terminal X to the multiplier. An additional address GT involves the selection of relay No. 85 which also connects Y to the multiplier.

The wealth of instructions which a digital computer can handle can be appreciated by relating the simple illustration of Fig. 7-5 to the number of switches represented in Fig. 7-4. Hence, in programming, the operational part of the instructions to the computer can channel information into and out of drum or tape storage, can send numbers to accumulators, and can channel input information to various multipliers, dividers, adders, or other calculation circuits as required.

A matrix can also be made up of and-circuits as shown in Fig. 7-6, and is useful for channeling information for storage to magnetic drums. Only nine and-gates are shown, though any number can be employed as required. Symbol designations for the vertical input lines could consist of the entire alphabet from A to Z, while the horizontal lines can be designated from 1 to 26. The output from each of the nine and-gates is connected to the recording head

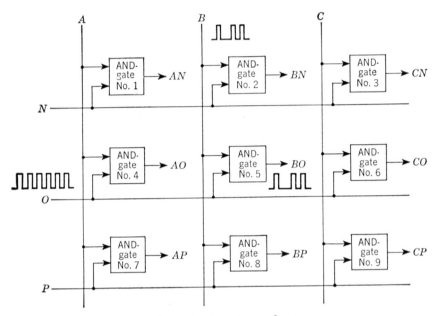

Fig. 7-6. Matrix using and-gates.

of a magnetic storage system, and as explained earlier, each recording head is a separate and independent channel on a magnetic drum type memory system. Thus, and-gate No. 1 has its output identified as AN, and any signal information from the output of and-gate No. 1 will be applied to the AN channel of the drum. Similarly, the output from and-gate No. 2 would be applied to the drum channel designated as BN.

As described earlier, an and-gate will have no output unless each input receives a pulse simultaneously. Thus, any and-circuit can be gated to permit an output providing both inputs are present. If, for instance, the binary number 1011 were to be stored in memory location BO, a series of continuous pulses would be applied to the input line O from the master generator, and the binary number 1011 applied to the B input line of the matrix. The binary number applied to the B line would consist of a serial train, and as each digit arrived at the input to the and-gate a series of pulses would also be applied to the second input of and-gate No. 5. In consequence, the binary pulses 1011 would appear at the output of the and-gate No. 5 and would be applied in sequence to the recording head of the magnetic storage device.

Another form which the switching network can assume is that shown in Fig. 7-7. Here, one particular signal can be channeled

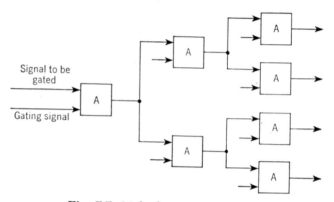

Fig. 7-7. Multiple-output switching.

through various and-gates to as many locations as desired. In the illustration shown, four output terminals are available for applying the original signal to any four other units. If desired, of course, the output and-gates can apply the signals to additional and-gates so that the original signal can be applied to as many other devices as may be necessary.

BURROUGHS PINBOARDS

The Burroughs Corporation employs the matrix principle in their Model E-101 computer to facilitate programming. The matrices are in the form of pinboards of lightweight frames somewhat resembling the boards used when playing the cribbage game. The pinboards are made up of three sections, each containing vertical and horizontal rows of small holes. The first section and a segment of the second section are shown in Fig. 7-8. Each row across the pinboard handles one instruction, thus permitting a total of sixteen instruc-

tions to be placed on one pinboard. The first section of the pinboard relates to the operation to be performed, such as multiplication, division, or subtraction. The second and third areas of the
pinboard are utilized for indicating the location of the memory section to be utilized during the programming.

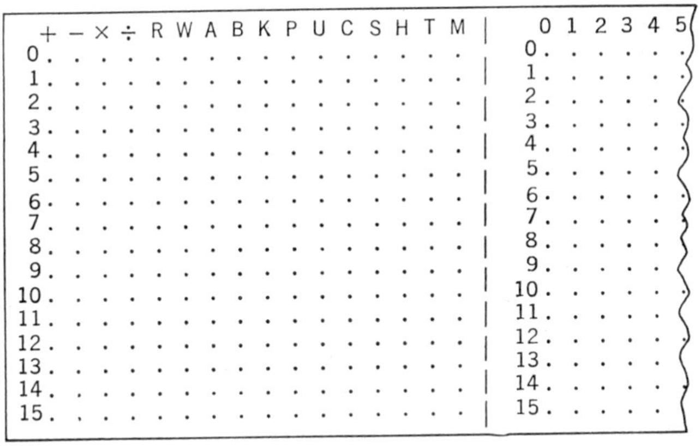

```
    + − × ÷ R W A B K P U C S H T M  |   0 1 2 3 4 5
 0 . . . . . . . . . . . . . . . . .  |  0 . . . . . .
 1 . . . . . . . . . . . . . . . . .  |  1 . . . . . .
 2 . . . . . . . . . . . . . . . . .  |  2 . . . . . .
 3 . . . . . . . . . . . . . . . . .  |  3 . . . . . .
 4 . . . . . . . . . . . . . . . . .  |  4 . . . . . .
 5 . . . . . . . . . . . . . . . . .  |  5 . . . . . .
 6 . . . . . . . . . . . . . . . . .  |  6 . . . . . .
 7 . . . . . . . . . . . . . . . . .  |  7 . . . . . .
 8 . . . . . . . . . . . . . . . . .  |  8 . . . . . .
 9 . . . . . . . . . . . . . . . . .  |  9 . . . . . .
10 . . . . . . . . . . . . . . . . .  | 10 . . . . . .
11 . . . . . . . . . . . . . . . . .  | 11 . . . . . .
12 . . . . . . . . . . . . . . . . .  | 12 . . . . . .
13 . . . . . . . . . . . . . . . . .  | 13 . . . . . .
14 . . . . . . . . . . . . . . . . .  | 14 . . . . . .
15 . . . . . . . . . . . . . . . . .  | 15 . . . . . .
```

Fig. 7-8. Detail of Burroughs computer pinboard matrix.

Each pinboard follows the matrix principle as previously explained, and a magnified view of a section of a pinboard is shown
in Fig. 7-9. As can be seen, independent upper horizontal strips

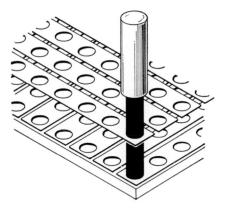

Fig. 7-9. Pinboard detail.

are isolated from independent lower strips at right angles to the
upper. When a pin or plunger is inserted, contact is made between

Fig. 7-10. Pinboards in Burroughs Model E-101 computer.

upper and lower strips in typical matrix fashion. Thus, in programming, a pin is inserted in the hole that represents a particular instruction making up the program, as shown by the example given later in this chapter. When all the pins have been placed in the pinboard to make up the particular program of instructions, the pinboards are inserted into the rack of the E-101 computer which accommodates a total of eight pinboards. Fig. 7-10 shows the pinboards in place in the computer. When the pinboards have been inserted into the rack, the computer will automatically follow each instruction in sequence unless instructed to do otherwise.

For convenience in programming, prepunched templates are provided which can be employed when making up the program. These

Fig. 7-11. Placing assembled pinboards into position.
(Courtesy of Burroughs Corp.)

templates are thin flexible sheets which have the same sixteen horizontal rows of tiny holes that the pinboards have. The template sheets also have the same identifying markings corresponding exactly to the pinboards themselves. The templates facilitate the initial programming procedures and permit a permanent record of a program to be retained. The various pin locations can be marked on the template initially, and when the program has been made up the template is placed on the pinboard and the pins are dropped into place. After that the assembled pinboards are placed into the computer, as shown in Fig. 7-11. After a problem has been solved by the computer, the pinboards may be removed and stored without disturbing the particular program. Thus, the identical program can be rerun at a later date. If, however, the particular program will not be used again for some time, the pins may be removed and only the templates filed for subsequent use. This permits the storing of the program while freeing the pinboards and pins for reuse in other problems and programs.

CARD INPUT

Information is stored on a card by punching holes in certain parts of the card which correspond to the information which is to be recorded. The cards are punched by inserting them in an appropriate key punch machine and depressing the necessary keys which will punch specific holes in particular locations on the card. A representative type of card is illustrated in Fig. 7-12, though most

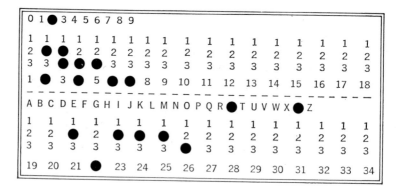

Fig. 7-12. Card punch read-in.

cards used in connection with digital computers contain more numbers than are shown.

The representative symbols which are printed on a card for a guide vary among the different manufacturers, and hence the processing of a card for a particular computer would involve familiarization with the printed symbols on the card. The cards themselves represent a form of storage device, since once the card is punched to contain a certain amount of information the cards can be stored and reused as required. Thus, a single card may contain the location of several storage sections on a drum, or it may specify that the computer perform certain operations. It may also contain the multiplicand and multiplier numbers which are involved in a multiplication calculation, or other numerical, alphabetical, or alpha-numerical instructions.

When the card is inserted into the digital computer input system, the information from the card is read into the computer. The read-in unit of the computer will scan the card area by "feelers" resembling miniature wire brushes, and will thus relay the information gathered by the sensing process. Thus, the hole patterns in the card can represent a binary digit pattern, and the information on the card can be channeled into the computer and stored in a magnetic drum system, if desired, for future use. Conversely, the stored information on a drum can be read out of the latter and transferred into the punch guide unit, which will then punch appropriate holes in a card. Thus, a card can be used to read the information to the computer, or material from within the computer such as stored information, or the results of a calculation can be read out and placed on cards for filing and future use as required.

The number of characters on a card depends on the extent of information which can be handled by a particular computer, and is also related to the complexity of the calculations which the computer can perform. If a computer is capable of performing only the fundamental calculations of addition, subtraction, multiplication, and division, other arithmetical routines (called subroutines) can be punched on a card for use as required. Thus, the information which is necessary for the machine to perform square root or the calculation of other similar equations can be stored on a card for use as required.

ADDRESS

Instructions which make up a program must give the computer a step-by-step procedure which it is to follow for the conclusion of a particular problem or calculation. For example, if multiplication is involved, the machine must be told which numbers to multiply. The multiplicand, for instance, may already be stored along with other numbers in a memory system. The multiplier, on the other hand, may be inserted in the accumulator. Then, the machine would have to be told to seek out the multiplicand located in a specific section of the memory and multiply the numbers found there by the numbers stored in the accumulator. The *location* of the multiplicand must be designated by symbols or numbers. Such symbols are codes which designate the localization of a particular section in the memory or storage system, and are known as an *address*, as previously mentioned. The address thus usually consists of several numbers which localize the particular memory area desired for a particular problem. Hence, location of this particular memory may be designated by address symbols such as 01, AS, 156, etc., depending on whether letters or numbers are used to form the address information.

An address can also be used for channeling the output from the computer to a specific unit such as a printer, magnetic memory, or card punch. The instruction for a particular computer can contain one or more addresses.

From the foregoing it can then be seen that an *instruction* contains information consisting of the *operation* part as well as the *address* part.

A single-address computer is defined as one in which one instruction contains only one address, which identifies *one* of the two numbers used in the computer (usually in storage location). The other number may be in the accumulator, and the result of the computation will also appear in the accumulator. This process of indicating operations sequentially is known as a "one-address' or "single-address" *code*.

A two-address computer is one wherein one address indicates

the location of a memory point, and the second address might indicate the location of the nature of the next instruction.

A three-address system is usually one in which all three addresses are operation locations. Sometimes, however, a three-address system is one in which the first two addresses consist of the operation, and the last address indicates the destination (or storage) of the results of the first two operations. The first symbol (several identifying digits) would be the address of the first operand, and the third address the location to which the result of the operations is to go.

In the four-address system the instruction contains an explicit statement which designates where the next instruction is located in the memory. Such a statement is the last address of the four-address instruction. (In the three-address system there is no such explicit statement regarding where the next instruction is located in the storage unit.) In some of the largest computers an address may consist of as many as sixteen binary digits so that it can find any one of thousands of storage locations.

A *floating* address is one which permits a subroutine to be placed anywhere in the memory automatically. A subroutine is a program involving calculations of basic functions such as square roots, logarithms, trigonometrical functions, etc. involving utilization of basic arithmetic steps. A computer, for instance, may have addition, subtraction, multiplication and division built in as a basic routine, but may not have a square root routine. The latter then becomes a subroutine process and must be programmed into the computer using in sequence the basic arithmetic steps already present in the computer. Of course, if square root can be solved as a basic function of the computer, then square root is not a subroutine process.

The Librascope machine is a single-address type of computer. The accumulator supplies one operand and holds the result of all the arithmetical operations. The LGP-30 is a "stored program" type of computer wherein the instructions are stored in the memory along with the data, and automatically obtained from the memory and utilized in the calculations in the specified sequence required for the calculations.

The Elecom 125 is a two-address computer, while the Raycom is a three-address system. The Monrobot computer is a four-address type.

WORD

In digital computers, a *word* applies to any group of digits which are handled as a single group and not as individual units. A particular digital computer may be designed to have eight digits in a word, while another digital computer may be designed to have fewer or more digits in a word. A particular number such as the binary number 101 (5) is considered as a word when this number is to be a multiplicand, a divisor, or another operational unit. Hence, word lengths will vary from one computer to another.

Storage devices are capable of retaining many words since each unit stores one word of a dozen or so digits (a binary digit is known as a *bit*). When a word is stored it can consist of a number or an address instruction. All words are preceded by a polarity sign.

TRANSFER

Transfer is the ability of a digital computer to interrupt its progress through a series of sequential operations and repeat a previous instruction. Transfer permits the computer to repeat an instruction one or more times. With the transfer feature, the computer can also repeat the entire program a given number of required times. Thus, a program with some fifty instructions might have included therein a command for the computer to repeat the initial six instructions. On the other hand, the last instruction of a program might indicate that the computer is to "transfer" to the beginning and repeat the entire program.

There are two kinds of transfers—*conditional* and *unconditional*. The conditional transfer involves a "decision" on the part of the computer, for the conditional transfer means that a certain transfer is to be made *provided* that some particular condition occurs prior to the time the transfer is to be made. Thus, a particular result may mean that there is no transfer to be made, while another result (a larger number than a designated one, or a minus sign instead of a plus sign, etc.) indicates that a transfer is to be made. A computer also has the ability to change or modify a given set of instructions, when such a change or modification is necessary for correct solution of the problem. This again involves *decision* processes, using and-gates or other comparator type circuitry.

The unconditional transfer means that a specific instruction is involved which causes the machine to go back to a definite previous instruction.

BREAKPOINT

Breakpoint operation is another programming feature often used. Breakpoint refers to that part of the program routine in which the operations of the computer processes are interrupted, even though the computer has not yet completed the work involved in the entire program. The interruption (breakpoint) is utilized for the purpose of checking the status of the instructions which have been performed up to the time of breakpoint.

A *conditional breakpoint instruction* is sometimes used in programming so that the computer operation is interrupted if a certain set of conditions exist. As with conditional transfer, the conditional breakpoint may or may not occur during the computer's operation, depending on the results of the computations up to the time of the conditional breakpoint instruction. The computer, by use of decision elements involving coincidence and comparator circuits, interprets the results of the computations preceding the breakpoint instruction. If a breakpoint is indicated the computer operations stop; if not, the program routine continues.

PROGRAMMING EXAMPLES

As mentioned earlier, programming procedures differ for the various computers, as do the address symbols, memory storage locations, etc. For familiarization with the general processes involved, however, a few typical examples of the programming of simple problems are given here. These illustrations will establish the routines involved in setting up the sequence of operations to be performed and the particular instructions which must be given the computer.

The first typical example involving programming applies to the

Readix Digital Computer. The Readix computer input information can be fed into the machine by the Flexowriter (discussed later in this chapter) or by use of magnetic tape, a paper tape reader, or an IBM card reader. The Readix has a fairly large list of instructions (commands) available for programming purposes. Even though the majority of problems can be programmed by use of a small number of instructions, the additional instructions available make for greater flexibility in the solving of complex equations.

In the Readix, two complete instructions can be stored in each computer word, affording some saving in storage requirements when programming is lengthy. For the purposes of the programming illustration, the following basic instructions are listed with their identifying numerical symbols:

Numerical Symbol	INSTRUCTION
29	Copy the number in the memory indicated by the address to the T register.
09	Copy the number in the S register into the memory position indicated by the address.
51	Exchange the two numbers which are in the T and S registers.
30	Reverse the sign of the number in the S register.
68	Add to the number in the S register the number in the memory indicated by the address. Leave answer in S.
28	Subtract from the number in the S register the number in the memory indicated by the address. Leave answer in S.
26	Multiply the number in the T register by the number in the memory indicated by the address. Leave answer in S.
76	Divide the number in the S register by the number in the memory indicated by the address. Leave answer in T.

The S register referred to above is an accumulator used in addition and subtraction. An *addition* command, for instance, will add a number to the contents of the S register and leave the sum there. In association with the T register, the S register can shift right or left as a twenty-digit word, permitting multiplication and division by means of addition or subtraction of other registers, using appropriate shifting.

Let us assume a problem consisting of the following:

$$\frac{(5 \times 4) - 2}{6} = ?$$

The individual numbers and processes could, of course, be applied to the computer in proper sequence, such as inserting 5 into the memory, 4 into the accumulator, then commanding the computer to multiply the two, etc. Preferably, however, the numbers involved in the computation should be stored in the memory and the computer given a sequence of commands in accordance with the numerical symbols given earlier for the Readix Computer. For convenience in referring to the values of the problem numbers, the equation for the example problem is given:

$$\frac{(a \times b) - c}{d} = y$$

Assume, then, that the numerical values involved in the problem have been stored in memory locations as follows for the initial programming step:

Symbol	Numerical Value	Memory Location Address
a	5	002
b	4	006
c	2	110
d	6	014
y	?	018

In placing the numerical values involved in the problem into storage, we had to select storage locations which we knew were not already occupied by information stored previously. Certain storage locations may contain information relating to some other problem, though in most instances the storage of information which is to be held for some time is done by utilizing auxiliary storage systems such as tape. For storage of data needed during the solving of a problem, magnetic drums or ferrite core matrix systems would be employed. Once we have ascertained which storage locations are available to us, we would proceed to enter the numerical values involved in the problem into specific storage locations. This entering of the numbers could be done by a keyboard read-in device, punched cards, etc. The individual number is not only read into the machine, but the particular address is given. Thus, in the foregoing example, the number 5 in the equation was placed in memory location 002, the number 4 into memory location 006, etc.

When each number of the equation has been entered into a particular rapid-access storage location, the instructions which tell the machine what to do with the stored numbers are entered (read-in). The instructions are also coded, as mentioned earlier, so we must select the particular instructional code which will tell the machine what is to be done with the stored numbers and in the sequence such processes must follow.

To enter the proper instructions into the machine, reference must be made to the symbols used in the machine's instructional code. Referring to the list of instructions given earlier for the Readix computer, note that the first instruction is coded by the symbol 29. When this symbol instruction is entered into the computer it must be accompanied by a storage address. The instruction symbol, plus the storage address, causes the computer to remove the number stored in the location specified, and place such a number into one of the computer registers (the T register). Thus, the number is placed into the calculation circuitry of the computer in readiness for mathematical processing. Hence, in programming our original equation, we would write down the symbols 29002 as our first set of instructions to the machine. The symbol 29 will cause our numerical value of 5 in our equation to be removed from storage location 002 and placed in the T register. Now we are ready to indicate the multiplication of $a \times b$.

Looking down the list of Readix instructions, we note that the numerical symbol 26 instructs the computer to multiply the number in the T register by the number in whatever storage location is specified in conjunction with symbol 26. Hence, we write down 26006 for the second step in our program of the equation. Thus, we instruct the computer to multiply the number 5 in the T register by the number 4 in storage location 006. The instruction symbol 26 also specifies to the computer that the product of the multiplication is to be placed in another register (S register) so that the number is in readiness for additional arithmetical processes.

So far, we have written down the first two steps in the program for the formula $(a \times b) - c/d$. It must be remembered that these two steps would not yet be read into the computer. The first job is to write down the entire sequence of steps in accordance with the mathematical procedures necessary, and in accordance with the identifying symbols for the particular computer. The next step, accordingly, is to program the process of subtracting c (numerical value 2 stored in memory location 110) from the product of $a \times b$. Again referring to the numerically coded list of instructions, we find that the symbol 28 initiates the subtraction process in the computer. Hence, we write down 28110 to indicate that the number stored in memory location 110 is to be subtracted from the number in the S register, leaving the answer in the S register.

In continuing to program the equation, 76014 is employed to initiate the division process with respect to the number stored in memory location 014. The instruction symbol 76 causes the machine to perform the division and leaves the answer in the T register. Some registers in computers, however, can only exchange information with other registers and may not be able to channel their contents to the drum or ferrite storage devices. If the mathematical process is completed and the information is to be read-out directly (or placed in storage for future usage) it may be necessary to place the information held by one register into some other register which has read-out facilities to storage, to printers, electric typewriters, etc. Thus, in our programming example it is expedient to take the information out of the T register and place it in the S register.

Reference to the numerically coded instruction list indicates that the symbol 51 may be used for exchanging the contents of the T and S registers. Thus, our next step is to program the symbol 51 in conjunction with three zeros (000). (No memory location is attached to the symbol 51 because the symbol simply causes the computer to exchange the contents of the S and T registers.) This step will place the answer to our equation into the S register, from which the number can be placed into storage or read-out as desired. Assuming we wish to place the answer to our equation into storage, we would use the symbol 09, because this symbol instructs the computer to copy whatever number is in the S register into the memory location indicated by the address symbol attached to the instruction symbol. If we decide to place the answer into address location 018, our final program instruction would be 09018.

The preceding discussion is a step-by-step analysis of the programming procedure; the actual program would not take as long to make up as might be inferred by the analysis. The complete program set-up follows—again, it looks more complex than it actually is because the explanatory operations are given. The actual material of this program which would be entered into the computer consists only of the instructional symbols shown at the left (29002, 26006, 28110, etc.).

Instruction	OPERATION
29002	Takes a (5) from the memory location address (002) and places it in the T register.
26006	Multiplies a by b and leaves the product in the S register (accumulator).
28110	Subtracts c from the $a \times b$ product and leaves the remainder in the S register.
76014	Divides the foregoing remainder by d and leaves y in the T register. (The numerical answer to the problem has now been procured by the computer and for the problem, is 3.)
51000	Exchanges S and T, leaving y in the S register.
09018	Stores the answer y in memory location 018.

The foregoing example utilizes only a few of the many instructions available, but gives a general idea of the programming processes involved with the Readix. Other instructions (commands) for the Readix include the arithmetic instruction for solving square root, a number of logical instructions involving decision flip-flop circuits and transfers, plus instructions involving the reading of tape, the writing of tape, punching or reading cards, etc.

To show the difference in the type of address symbols used, consider the programming of a similar problem with respect to the Alwac III digital computer. A partial list of some of the alphanumerical symbols used for instructions consists of the following:

Symbol	INSTRUCTION
e6	Multiply contents of B register by word given by address.
ea	Perform long division process.
30	Exchange the B and A registers (interchanges information).
36	Exchange the E and A registers (interchanges information).
40	Copy information stored in W register into B register.
48	Copy information stored in A register into W register.

Using some of the few instructions given above, consider the programming of the following problem:

$$\frac{30 \times 2}{12} = ?,$$

$$\frac{a \times b}{c} = y$$

As in the preceding example, the numerical values are put into the storage system. Any storage locations would suffice, and the following are given as representative:

Symbol	Numerical Value	Memory Location Address
a	30	40
b	2	42
c	12	44

Inasmuch as each order and each address in the Alwac III is represented by two characters, the resulting programming sequence and code would be as follows for the foregoing simple problem:

Instructional Command	OPERATION
40 40	Copy word in storage location 40 into the B register.
e6 42	Multiply the information in the B register by word in storage location 42.
ea 44	Divide product obtained by preceding step by word in storage location 44.
30 __	Exchange A and B (remainder and quotient) quotient now in A.
48 40	Copy the A register into word 40 [replaces the a (numerical value of 30) in memory location No. 40 by the result $(y = 5)$.]

Programming for the Burroughs Model E-101 computer employs as the input an eleven-column full keyboard of the Burroughs bookkeeping machine (see next chapter) plus the pinboards previously described. The various numerical portions of the problem are entered on the keyboard and then are processed by the instructions which have been placed on the pinboards. If a pin is inserted under the *K* symbol of the pinboard, it will instruct the computer to transfer the contents of the keyboard into the accumulator. Initially the operator entered the information into the keyboard, and the *K* instruction on the pinboard will transfer the contents of the keyboard into the accumulator when the operator depresses the motor bar on the keyboard. If a series of other instructions precedes the *K* instruction, the computer will perform the various steps required. When it reaches the *K* instruction, the computer will stop and the keyboard light will flash, notifying the operator that the machine is ready for the keyboard entry. The number can then be entered in the keyboard and the keyboard motor bar depressed. The number is then automatically channeled into the accumulator and the keyboard mechanism prints it out. Four motor bars are employed, each one moving the carriage in a different way so that the place on the type-out material can be controlled. The motor bars are also employed for printing out, and again, each one will print in a different manner. Motor bar *P2*, for instance, is used to print across the report horizontally, while depressing motor bar *P3* instructs the computer to print numbers in a vertical column. The computer prints directly on any form of document, such as a ledger card, duplicating master, or any other form, without the necessity of recopying. With the E-101 computer, data may also be entered into the accumulator by punched tape by use of an optional tape input unit.

Fig. 7-13 shows a sectional portion of a pinboard which has been programmed. Each pinboard is divided into three areas, as previously mentioned. The first area has room for sixteen instructions of addition, multiplication, division, subtraction, etc. The second area is for indicating the first digit of the memory location while the third area identifies the second digit of the memory location. In areas No. 2 and No. 3 there are also alphabetical designations, in addition to those in area No. 1. If a pin is placed under *K* as shown by the larger dot in Fig. 7-13, it will instruct the computer to transfer the contents of the keyboard into the accumulator when the

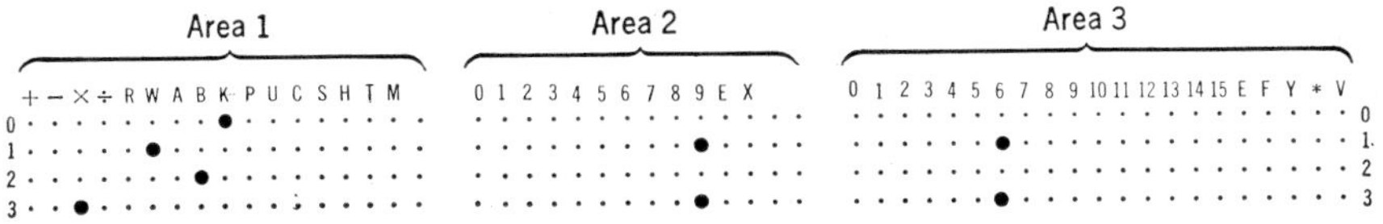

Area 1	Area 2	Area 3

```
      + − × ÷ R W A B K P U C S H T M      0 1 2 3 4 5 6 7 8 9 E X      0 1 2 3 4 5 6 7 8 9 10 11 12 13 14 15 E F Y * V
  0   · · · · · · · · ● · · · · · · ·      · · · · · · · · · · · ·      · · · · · · · · · · · · · · · · · · · · · ·   0
  1   · · · · · ● · · · · · · · · · ·      · · · · · · · · · ● · · ·      · · · · · · · · · · · · · · · · · · · · · ·   1.
  2   · · · · · · · ● · · · · · · · ·      · · · · · · · · · ● · · ·      · · · · · · · ● · · · · · · · · · · · · · ·   2
  3   · · ● · · · · · · · · · · · · ·      · · · · · · · · · ● · · ·      · · · · · · ● · · · · · · · · · · · · · · ·   3
```

Fig. 7-13. Pinboard programming.

operator depresses a motor bar as previously mentioned. Note that no pins are in the first horizontal rows of either area No. 2 or area No. 3. In area No. 1, a pin is indicated under *W* and along the same horizontal row a pin is indicated under the 9 in area No. 2 and under the 6 in area No. 3. This instructs the computer to enter the contents of the accumulator into the memory location No. 96, leaving a copy in the accumulator. In the third horizontal column in area No. 1, a pin is inserted under *B* which instructs the computer to transfer the contents of the accumulator into the *B* register, while still leaving a copy in the accumulator. The next step, along the third horizontal lines of the areas, shows a pin under the *X* in area No. 1, and also a pin under the 9 in area No. 2 and the 6 in area No. 3. This instruction informs the computer to multiply the contents of the *B* register by the contents of memory location No. 96, leaving the remainder in the accumulator. The computer has now taken the number and performed a squaring function. If the number were 9, for instance, the remainder in the accumulator would now be 81.

The foregoing is a brief example of the manner in which a program is inserted into the pinboards. Many other operations can, of course, be performed as indicated by the various alphabetical symbols of the pinboard. Besides the arithmetic processes, the other processes are included: if, for instance, *R* 98 were placed across the horizontal areas of the pinboard, it would instruct the computer to read the contents of memory location No. 98 into the accumulator, leaving a copy in memory location No. 98. *W* copies the contents of the accumulator to be written into the memory location indicated by the numbers placed in the second and third pinboard areas.

The A letter in area No. 1 is for shifting the contents of the accumulator. A 11, for instance, shifts the contents of the accumulator one place to the left. A 21, for instance, shifts the contents of the accumulator one place to the right. If A is used in conjunction with the asterisk in area No. 3, it would instruct the computer to halt the processes and the machine stops. Instruction B in area No. 1 transfers the contents of the accumulator into the B register, leaving a copy in the accumulator, as previously mentioned. K, as was previously mentioned, transfers the contents of the keyboard into the accumulator. The P symbol in area No. 1 instructs the computer to print the contents of the accumulator in the fashion indicated by motor bar No. 1, No. 2, etc.

The U designation in area No. 1 denotes the unconditional transfer while the C denotes the conditional transfer. The S instruction in area No. 1 is a decision element which can cause the computer to repeat certain steps. Thus, an instruction involving the S symbol may indicate that if a certain sum is greater than a given number the next instruction should follow, but if the sum is identical to the given number some other process should be performed.

The H symbols are utilized in conjunction with the S and U instructions for the process known as *stepping*, where it is necessary to repeat certain steps over and over again in a particular computation. The T symbol refers to taped transfer. T 11, for instance, means to execute the next instruction on tape in sequence until control is returned to the pinboard by a U or C instruction on the tape. The instruction T 12 indicates that the computer is to read the next number on tape into the accumulator, and then continue with the next pinboard instruction.

COMMERCIAL INPUT-OUTPUT DEVICES

Besides the magnetic tape, punched cards, and the perforated boards previously described, other commercial devices are also available for reading in and reading out computer information. A few of the typical commercial units are described here for reference purposes and to illustrate the variety of equipment which makes for computer flexibility and operational convenience.

The Flexowriter, mentioned earlier, is a typical combination of an input-output device. It consists of an electric typewriter which has been adapted for use with digital computers, and is a product of the Commercial Controls Corporation of New York. As an input device, the instructions for the computer are typed out and the Flexowriter automatically punches a tape. A hole in the tape represents a specific bit of information which is picked up by the computer. For read-out purposes, the computations or answers furnished by the computer can be channeled into the Flexowriter and the latter will then type out the result.

Fig. 7-14. The Flexowriter.

The Flexowriter is shown in Fig. 7-14, and the keyboard is shown in Fig. 7-15. As can be seen, the main keys comprise a standard electric typewriter keyboard, providing both lower case and upper case letters. A backspace lever is provided, as well as the

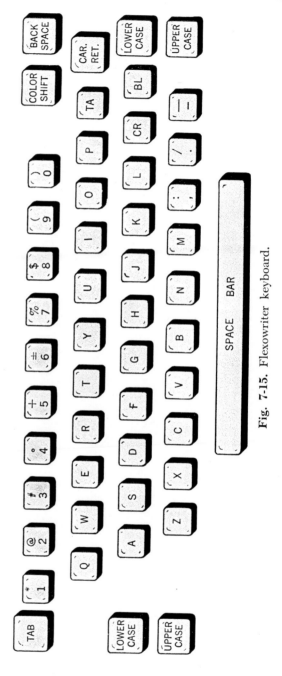

Fig. 7-15. Flexowriter keyboard.

carriage return and tabulation key. The color shift key is for use when a color ribbon is employed.

Above the regular keyboard are six controls, three at the upper left and three at the upper right. These six controls are utilized with respect to the paper tape used for instruction and programming purposes with the computer. The *start read* key is used to start the *reader* mechanism which moves the tape along during the punching in of a set of instructions or program. The *stop read* key is employed for manually stopping the reader mechanism, and this key is used principally on those occasions when the electric typewriter is operated independently of the computer.

The *punch-on* key is employed for the manual preparation of punched tapes. When the punch-on key is depressed, the Flexowriter will punch on the tape the corresponding character which is being typed on the paper in the typewriter. The punch-on key can be employed to prepare program tapes on the Flexowriter even when the latter is not directly connected to the computer. When connected to the computer, the punch-on key can also be used to punch a program tape while the program is being typed directly into the computer. Thus, the tape which is being prepared can be utilized later for duplicating the particular set of instructions. During the time the computer is operating, the material which is typed out by the Flexowriter under the command of the computer will also be punched on the tape at the same time.

The *tape feed* key is used in connection with the punch-on key to feed several inches of leader through the tape punch mechanism before the tape punching process is started. It can also be used to provide for several inches of blank trailing tape after a program has been recorded on the tape. While the tape feed button is depressed in conjunction with the punch-on, sprocket holes will be punched on the tape automatically at a rate of approximately ten holes per second for as long as the tape feed button is depressed. This provides a leader without any corresponding "date holes" being punched.

The *code delete* key is depressed when it is necessary to correct errors in the tape. When the wrong key has been depressed and the corresponding code hole punched in the tape, the tape is backed up to the first incorrect character and the "code deletes" holes are punched into the same position as the errors. After the incorrect characters have been deleted from the tape, the correct characters are then retyped.

The *stop code* key is used to punch a special symbol at the end of a complete set of instructions or program. This stop code signal can also be placed at the end of a particular group of data or instructions, as required.

A great many different combinations of auxiliary units are available with this machine so that it can be adapted to the various input systems of computers. Substantially any arrangement of keys can be provided on the keyboard. The standard Flexowriter is equipped with a 12-inch carriage which will accept an 11-inch wide sheet with a 9½-inch writing line. In addition, 16-inch and 20-inch carriages are available. Various platens are also available to obtain desired printing quality for such applications as stencil writing, multiple carbon copies, etc. Auxiliary contacts are also available for attachment to various points of the Flexowriter.

Some companies utilize their own electric typewriter inputs. One of these is the Bendix computer, Model G-15, which employs an electric tyepwriter known as the Master Writer, illustrated in Fig. 7-16. This device is mounted on a base containing switches and other devices for controlling the computer by depressing keys on the Master Writer. With the electric typewriter connected to the computer, the typing of information on the keyboard enters it directly into the computer as with the Flexowriter previously discussed. Hence, the Master Writer is used to start calculations, to initiate input commands and operations, to stop the computer, to read out in printed form the results of a calculation, or to control any of the other operations necessary. (See the next chapter.)

The reading out (read-out) process of a computer makes available any information which is contained in the storage sections of the computer, as well as the results of calculations which the computer has performed. Such information, however, must be converted from electric impulses into some form of a permanent record which is readily understood and identified. Besides read-out devices such as the printer, the electric typewriter, and punched cards, storage tubes are also available for displaying printed data on the face of a screen. Such tubes are of the cathode ray type similar to those used in television receivers, and the numerical or alphabetical information becomes visible on the screen.

Fig. 7-16. Master Writer input.
(Courtesy of Bendix Corp.)

The Oscilloscope Printer-Plotter, manufactured by Remington Rand Univac, has such a cathode ray tube which rapidly presents the results of digital computations by showing on the screen the results in the form of a graph, words, or numbers. The device is known as the Model 3061 and was developed for use with the Univac computer system Model ERA1103A, which is a general purpose digital computing system for applications which require large storage capacity, high operating speed, and programming facility.

The cathode ray tube used with the Printer-Plotter is 5 inches in diameter and has a flat surface so that there is a minimum of distortion. A medium-persistent phosphor is employed, so that the information which appears on the screen can be easily viewed or photographed for permanent recording when required.

The scanning beam is sharply focused and provides 65,536 different locations for a particular display dot visible on the screen. The maximum speed of illumination is 40,000 dots per second. The Printer-Plotter is available with a 35 mm automatic camera or a manually operated Polaroid Land camera. The Land camera provides a finished black and white picture in one minute after exposure and thus furnishes a permanent record of the information which appears on the picture tube face.

Another tube which is available for displaying printed data on the face of the screen is the Typotron obtainable from Hughes Products, a division of the Hughes Aircraft Company. A choice of sixty-three characters is available for presentation of data in words, numbers, or symbols on the screen. When used as a high speed digital read-out unit, the Typotron writes characters $\frac{1}{8}$ inch in size on the screen at speeds of at least 25,000 characters per second.

Figure 7-17 is an illustration of the tube face of a Typotron showing all the available characters. Besides the characters shown, the device can also be utilized to show patterns in similar fashion to the performance of an oscilloscope tube. The information appearing on the face of the tube remains visible for as long as desired.

The Typotron tube has an internal thin metal stencil (the character matrix) which incorporates sixty-three characters. Other matrices are available or can be manufactured if necessary. An electron beam passes through the matrix and is directed by selection plates within the tube to the desired character which is to be reproduced on the front of the screen. Any one, or any combination of the sixty-three characters can be written sequentially and displayed continuously until erased.

The type of phosphor used is green, P-1, and both the focusing and deflection processes are electrostatic in nature. The imaging of characters is accomplished by magnetic means. The tube has a usable screen diameter of 4 inches and may be mounted in any position.

Devices for displaying numbers only are also available for use with digital computers. One such device is the CMC In-Line Read-Out instrument, Model 401A. This is manufactured by the Computer-Measurements Corporation, a subsidiary of Hancock Manu-

Fig. 7-17. Character display on typotron tube.
(Courtesy of Hughes Aircraft Co.)

facturing Company. This device is housed in a cabinet $4\frac{1}{2}$ inches high, 17 inches wide, and $17\frac{1}{2}$ inches deep. The display section incorporates a number of neon lamps which light up to indicate any number up to a six-digit capacity. Since each number is displayed by a group of neon lamps, a particular lamp failure will not destroy the indication. Individual numerals are $2\frac{1}{2}$ inches high. If desired, several of these units can be connected to a single digital computer for simultaneous multiple usage. The instrument has an internal storage device which changes only upon the receipt of instructions from the computer to which the unit is attached. Figure 7-18 shows a typical display on the Model 401A panel.

Fig. 7-18. CMC Model 401A panel.
(Courtesy of Computer Measurements Corp.)

In another device for displaying numbers is the Nixie electronic indicating tube manufactured by the Electronic Tube Division of the Burroughs Corporation. This is a small tube having a diameter of 1 inch and a height of 1 inch. The Nixie is a gas filled, cold cathode tube. Glow wires within the tube form the various digits from 0 to 9. Each wire, forming a single digit in shape, is connected to a separate prong of the tube. Thus, by the application of the proper potentials to the tube prongs, any number between 0 and

9 will appear as a lighted area within the tube. Only the number selected appears when the tube is functioning. Thus, a number of these tubes can be utilized to indicate a series of digits which make up a particular number. Since any other tube can display any number from 0 to 9, a row of such tubes can display any group of numbers up to the limit of the number of tubes employed. The tube is useful for displaying the numbers in counters as well as for displaying other numbers decimally in a digital computer.

Also available are a number of printers which print graphs, charts, or the results of computations directly on paper fed into the machine from large rolls. Previously, it was mentioned that the Flexowriter is also utilized as a print-out device since it can be operated under the direct control of the computer, and will not only print the required information but will also punch a running tape which can be reused at a later time as required. Another form of printer is the electromechanical type, a typical example of which is the one used in the RCA-developed electronic data-processing computer known as the Bizmac. The printer is shown in Fig. 7-19, and this forms the Bizmac output device which prints an original and three carbon copies of finished paper work at a speed of 600 lines per minute. The electronic control unit for the electromechanical printer is shown at the right and rear of the printer mechanism.

Questions Relating to Chapter 7

1. Briefly explain what is meant by a computer "program."

2. Show by a simple schematic the construction of a matrix utilizing and-circuits.

3. Define the terms single-address, two-address, and three-address.

4. What is meant by a "word" with respect to digital computers?

5. What is meant by "transfer" and what two types are generally found in digital computers?

6. Program the following formula either for the Readix or Alwac III computers, assigning appropriate memory location symbols:

$$\frac{(a - b) \times c}{d} = y$$

Fig. 7-19. Printer in the Bizmac computer. (Courtesy of RCA.)

7. Briefly describe a pinboard matrix and give the symbolic instructions for the problem $a + b = c$. Assign appropriate memory location symbols.

8. When an electric typewriter such as the Flexowriter is employed, what processes are started by depressing the start read key and the stop read key?

9. What are the purposes for a punch-on key, the tape feed key, the code delete key, and the stop code key in the Flexowriter?

10. How many different locations for any particular display dot are incorporated in the Oscilloscope Printer-Plotter of the Univac?

11. List some of the characteristics of the Typotron and its application in digital computers.

12. How many printed copies are available from the Bizmac printer and what is the printing speed?

8

□ □ □
□ □ □
□ ■ □

Commercial Computers

INTRODUCTION

There is a variety of computers available for industrial applications. Several such computers are designed to perform tasks which are of a sufficiently routine nature that they can be adapted to the requirements of many industries. Many of the basic functions are those of addition, subtraction, multiplication, and division and hence they can take over the jobs of accounting procedures. When more complex types of calculations are required, such as square root, the processes can either be built in or programmed on cards or templates that can be filed for use in the future.

Also available are many industrial computers which can undertake filing procedures and retain information which is readily available because of the rapid access time in storage devices. Computers are, of course, capable of being linked with automatic devices such as printers, sorters, and other discriminatory devices which will perform certain tasks under the command of the computer as the latter performs the specific computations. In complex accounting and payroll setups, for instance, time cards of employees can be punched (perforated) instead of printed, as is often the case; and when the perforated cards are fed into a digital computer, the latter will interpret the perforations in terms of the number of hours worked by a particular employee. The computations would also involve the calculations for ascertaining the withholding tax deductions, social security deductions, unemployment compensation deductions, hospitalization deductions, etc. Once the computer has obtained the individual figures, it can then prepare a paycheck. The fixed perforations on the time card trip the appropriate selector relays which will then print the employee's name on the pay check by selecting the proper address plate and feeding it to the printer. The individual sums representing the net pay, plus the deductions, are also printed on the check. The computer can also be designed so that an envelope is printed at the same time and the check inserted in the envelope.

Special type computers are also designed to do specific jobs when the processes are of such a nature that they are nonstandard. Computers can be utilized, for instance, to maintain a running file on the seats which are available on particular flights in air travel companies. They can be designed in such a manner that they will immediately give information on which seats are available for any particular flight. Digital computers have also been found of particular benefit in storage and warehouse systems where it is necessary to have available the information regarding the items which are in storage. The computer can be designed to catalogue the various items in particular groups for identification, and will maintain a running inventory on the various items that are removed as well as on the new items which may be stored.

It is beyond the scope of this text to give a full and complete description of the capabilities of each industrial computer on the market, since there are many. Those described herein, however, have been chosen as indicative of the type which may be encountered in the field and hence representative of the functional aspects which will be found therein. All function on the principles heretofore detailed in this book. The number of circuits utilized, and the particular tasks which the computers perform are the essential differences.

IBM 705

Figure 8-1 illustrates the IBM 705 electronic data processing machine. This device is manufactured by the International Business Machines Corporation for the high speed processing of commerical data and for the solving of business problems. The input and output devices have a considerable amount of flexibility. Punched cards can be utilized for direct input, and stored information on magnetic tape may also be fed to the input. The information on punched cards can also be read directly into the magnetic memory by one or more card reading devices. Punched cards can also be created directly and line printers may be attached when printed reports and other documents are necessary. The same tape units that are used with the IBM 705 can also be utilized in connection with the card reading devices, the card punching devices or the line printers for independent operation. This minimizes the number of steps necessary for such processes and makes the system quite flexible.

The design of the 705 is such that programming is not excessively involved, and relatively inexperienced personnel can be utilized for such procedures. Sixteen separate accumulators are in the 705 for aiding the programming process. The instructions themselves include such simplified ones as "add to accumulator," etc.

In the Model 705, reading and writing are performed simultaneously at the rate of 15,000 characters per second. Input and output time can be reduced an additional amount by attachment of an optional magnetic core "record storage" device. The latter device provides extremely rapid accessibility to data stored therein, which can be transferred to and from the magnetic memory in less than 24 microseconds per character.

A number of magnetic tape reader-recorders can be employed with the Model 705. There are 2,400 feet of tape on one reel and information is recorded at 200 characters to the inch. Thus, a maximum capacity on one reel consists of more than 5,000,000 characters. This is equivalent to the contents of more than 60,000 punched cards on one reel of tape.

The card reader employed by the 705 operates at the rate of 250 cards per minute. Information from the cards is read into a

Fig. 8-1. IBM Electronic Data Processing Machine. (Courtesy of IBM Corp.)

231

temporary storage in the control unit, and more than one card reader can be employed if desired. The printer utilized with the 705 is capable of printing 150 lines per minute. Each line may contain up to 120 numerical, alphabetical, or special characters. Carriage spacing, skipping, and other methods of operation can be controlled from the 705 unit or by the setting of dials on the carriage of the printer. The 705 may be provided with a number of printers. A printer and a tape unit may be connected together to provide direct tape-printer operation independent of the computing sections of the 705.

The card punch unit accepts data from the central processing unit and punches IBM cards at the rate of 100 per minute. Additional card punching machines can be employed with the 705 and as with the printer, direct tape-to-card operation can be employed independently of the computer circuitry.

In performing calculations of an arithmetic or logical operation, the 705 has exceptionally high speed. Addition or subtraction operations involving five-digit numbers can be completed in 120 microseconds. Multiplication can be performed in 800 microseconds, while division (six digits by five digits) can be done in less than 2 milliseconds. Calculations involving logical decisions are performed in 154 microseconds. The time elements include that required to locate and interpret the instructions anywhere in the magnetic core memory, and to locate and process such data.

A complementary unit to the 705 is the IBM 650 magnetic drum data processing machine shown in Fig. 8-2. The device consists of three units. The magnetic drum and the electronic calculating components are housed in two separate cabinets, one of which has incorporated into it an operating console. The third unit has provisions for input and output facilities. The data processing machine has been designed to meet the many computing and accounting requirements, in fields of operation which lie between those now served by the company's very large and complex calculators and its variety of smaller machines. The 650 processing machine has up to 20,000 memory positions which can be utilized for the storage of informational data as well as operating instructions.

The 650 magnetic core memory provides storage of the 20,000 characters in such a manner that the information is available at 3,528,000 characters per minute. Each of the 20,000 memory positions can be contacted individually at any time. Hence, they can

Fig. 8-2. Magnetic Drum Data Processing Machine.
(Courtesy of IBM Corp.)

be grouped to form fields of any size or records of any length. Each memory position is made up of seven cores to represent the seven binary bits on the seven tracks. All cores in a column are negative except those that make up the values stored in that column.

BENDIX G-15

The Bendix G-15 illustrated in Fig. 8-3 is an all-purpose computer system. Incorporated in the unit are: a general-purpose digital computer, a digital differential analyzer, and provisions for a wide selection of input and output devices such as paper tape, magnetic tape, punched cards, graphs, and printed copy.

The keyboard Master Writer shown on the portable stand in Fig. 8-3 is essentially an electric typewriter mounted on a base which contains switches and other control facilities. (See Fig. 7-16.) All operations of the computer are controlled from this Master Writer. Information may be entered into the computer directly from the keyboard, and the computer output may be tabulated by the Master Writer. The Master Writer is also employed to start com-

Fig. 8-3. Bendix G-15 Computer.
(Courtesy of Bendix Corp.)

putation, to initiate input operations, to stop computation, or to cause a single command to be executed. It is utilized to cause print-out of the accumulator or print-out of the next command entered. The Master Writer can also be used to control any of several other operations which may be found convenient to the operator or pro-grammer.

With respect to programming, interpretative codes are available and fully described in manuals which enable a person without com-puter experience or training to prepare a problem for solution by the Bendix G-15. These codes are lists of "orders" or instructions which simplify usage. A problem is programmed in terms of these orders, and a paper tape is punched to represent the orders along with the numerical constants associated with the particular prob-lem. Both the coded tape and the problem tape are then entered into the computer, using preloaded tape magazines and a high speed photo tape reader. In the Model G-15 the command utilized for programming is composed of eight independent parts. Each part represents only a portion of the total command. By spelling out the command, part by part, it is possible for the programmer to instruct the computer to do precisely what is wanted in a minimum of time. The magnetic drum memory includes twenty channels, each of 108-word capacity, four channels of 4-word capacity, three channels of 2-word capacity, and one channel of 1-word capacity. A command usually specifies the transfer of information from a source to a desti-nation.

A feature of the G-15 is the input-output system. An input or output operation for as many as 108 words may be initiated by a single comand and the operation will then proceed without inter-ruption until completed. During such a process the computer may continue to compute with full efficiency. This is in contrast to many computers where no computation can be accomplished during input or output procedures.

One to four magnetic tape units may be connected to each G-15 computer. Each tape unit is capable of storing 300,000 words of information on a single reel, and the tape may be scanned for in-formation at six times the reading or writing speed.

Equipment is also available for reading and punching cards di-rectly by the G-15 so that it can be integrated directly into a punch card data processing system.

Addition and subtraction processes can be performed in 0.54 millisecond, and multiplication and division in 16.7 milliseconds.

READIX

The Readix illustrated in Fig. 8-4 is a general-purpose computer manufactured by the J. B. Rea Company. Internal operation is in the decimal number system, with each decimal digit represented by four bits. This "binary coded decimal" system is utilized to simplify the coding of most problems. The system also simplifies the process involved in checking out new routines.

As standard equipment, the Readix is supplied with a Flexowriter electric typewriter shown at left of Fig. 8-4. The keyboard of this typewriter, as well as its paper tape reader, may be used for computer input. The six-hole paper tape coded by the Readix can be read at a speed of 10 digits per second.

The Readix will also accept the full or partial contents of IBM cards at the rate of 100 cards per minute. An IBM Model 523 reader-punch device is used to read the cards and transfer their data to a maximum of eight word spaces in the working storage of the computer.

The computer magnetic tape data storage unit can also be used as an input device. Photoelectric paper tape readers and other input devices can readily be adapted to the Readix.

The Readix, during the output cycle, can continue to compute and can be programmed for automatic output tabulation. Output can be punched into IBM cards at the rate of 100 cards per minute using the aforementioned 523 reader punch.

The magnetic tape storage reels have the capacity of 1,200 feet of $\frac{3}{8}$ inch tape. Words are grouped on the tape in blocks of forty with a block address recorded permanently for each block. Eight channels are recorded on the tape. Four channels are used for data storage. One contains a parity check on the first four to detect operational errors or tape defects, one contains a clock for the four data channels, and one contains the permanent block address clock. The eighth channel is a spare that may be used for special applications.

When a block search command is received from the computer, the tape unit searches in the proper direction until the desired

Fig. 8-4. The Readix Computer. (Courtesy of J. B. Rea Co.)

237

block address is found. Then the tape unit stops and waits for the computer to give a read or write command. When this command is received, forty words are read from or written on the tape block that has been found in the search.

After a block search command has been introduced into the Readix, the latter continues to compute while the block search is in progress. If a read or write order is given before the search is completed, the computer will idle until the tape unit locates the desired block. If a read or write order is given without a preceding block search order, the tape unit will read from or write on the next block in order on the tape.

Tape speed is 15 inches per second for reading or writing, and 60 inches per second for searching. Average access time in a random tape is 1.33 minutes. Access time can be greatly reduced in many problems by efficient programming, and in cases where data can be stored in the order in which it will later be required, access time is reduced to the time required for the tape to advance from one block to the next. Several tape units may be used with a single Readix computer, and all tape units can search simultaneously.

The Readix employs a complete set of commands plus a number of special operating features which simplify programming. The arithmetic commands include addition, subtraction, multiplication, division, and square root. The square root is a direct command, and not a routine.

The Readix will add in 10.44 milliseconds, and multiply in 25 milliseconds maximum with a 16-millisecond average. It will divide in 40 milliseconds maximum with 24 milliseconds average. Square root can be done in 70 milliseconds maximum, with 40 milliseconds average. There are 128 flip-flop circuits used, and 3,040 logical gate diodes, plus 132 other circuits such as read and write amplifiers, etc.

ELECOM 125

The Elecom 125 system illustrated in Fig. 8-5 is a computer designed expressly to handle general business applications. The Elecom 125 system consists of a general purpose electronic computer, and a file processor consisting of an automatic data handling

Fig. 8-5. Elecom File Processor and Computer. (Courtesy of Underwood Corp.)

unit which sorts, collates, selects, and categorizes information recorded on magnetic tape.

The Elecom is manufactured by the Electronic Computer Division of the Underwood Corporation. It includes a wide variety of input and output facilities and features a special drum memory, the facility to handle any number of magnetic-tape units, and automatic floating decimal operation.

The computer is capable of solving highly intricate scientific and engineering problems, hence it handles with ease the relatively simple arithmetic problems found in business applications.

Of the two pieces of the Elecom equipment which comprise the 125 system, the file processor is used for all sequencing operations. Thus, daily inputs of new data can be arranged in the same order as the main file. The file processor extracts from the voluminous "library tapes" shown in the rear panels of Fig. 8-5 the particular items shown to which processing is to be done; for instance, in inventory control work in any particular day it may be necessary to update several thousand of a total of some 20,000 accounts carried in the main file. The file procedure chooses the pertinent several thousand items out of the magnetic tape file so that the computer wastes no time in searching through unwanted items. Once the pertinent items have been processed by the computer section of the system, the file procedure replaces them in proper sequence in the main magnetic storage file.

Interrelated commands between the file processor and the computer are made through the medium of magnetic tape. A tape interconnecting panel switches the tape unit to and from the electronic computer and the file processor. The interconnecting panel eliminates needless reel changing and allows continuous flow of data between the two pieces of equipment. In the panel the output from one unit can be used as the input to the other, and vice versa.

In a typical business application such as inventory control, the 125 system does all the needed calculations. It deducts quantities shipped, adds quantities received, takes percentages, etc. On the other hand, it can solve simultaneous linear equations, perform trigonometric functions, and do similar calculations. Since it is a decimal machine, there is no input or output conversion from binary or other systems. Inasmuch as it is alphabetical as well as numerical, it can handle programmed alpha-numerical sequence operations, locate alpha-numerical indexing data, and store data and prepare reports involving both letters and figures. The file processor is an entirely separate piece of equipment and can be eliminated from the system if the application does not require the handling of large amounts of data.

The Elecom file processor contains 250 vacuum tubes and 2,500 crystal diodes. Internal memory consists of an acoustic quartz line with a maximum block length of 200 digits. Greater capacity is available if needed.

The magnetic tapes operate at 6,000 digits per second or about 5 minutes for a 1,200 foot reel of tape. A magnetic drum memory having a capacity of 4,000 words is furnished according to the users' needs. Access time in the main memory system is 8.3 milliseconds average. Arithmetic operations include addition and subtraction, with or without first clearing the accumulator, and with or without storing the result in the memory. Multiplication can be performed, with or without round-off.

The logical operations of the 125 computer consist of the transfer of a single word from one address to another, transfer of up to fifty consecutive words in either direction between the memory and the rapid access memory, financial edit operation for inserting decimal point before last two digits of a word, and special instructions to facilitate input editing.

Input-output operational characteristics include magnetic tape capacity for 2,000 characters per second, and punched card handling for 100 to 240 eighty-column cards per minute in reading, depending on the card reading equipment used. One hundred cards are handled during the punching process.

Punched tape, at normal speed, can handle 8 characters per second, either input or output. At high speed, the rate falls between 200 to 400 characters per second for input, and 60 characters per second for output. Printed tape handles 500 characters per second for the input.

DATATRON

The Datatron computer illustrated in Fig. 8-6 is manufactured by the Electro Data Company, an affiliate of Burroughs Corporation. The Datatron is an automatic digital computer which can be used to solve a wide variety of computations, data reduction, and information processing problems which arise in science, industry, and commerce. The numbers it operates on, and the numerical code instructions it obeys, are stored internally. The computer can compare numbers or instructions and change its sequence of operations accordingly, and even modify the instructions themselves as required.

Routines and subroutines are stored on perforated paper tape which is prepared with a small decimal keyboard or the keyboard of a Flexowriter. With the photoelectric tape reader, information can be read into the computer at over 500 decimal digits per second. A mechanical tape reader on a Flexowriter can also be used to read information in at a slower rate. The Flexowriter prints out numerical results directly from the computer at 10 characters per second. Upper and lower case alphabetical characters, punch marks, and other symbols on the Flexowriter keyboard are printed out with a format controlled unit which allows easy setting of line, paragraph, and page lengths. Flexowriter print-out may be recorded on perforated tape at the same time and rate as the Flexowriter prints out information.

A punched card converter can be utilized and the computer will handle alpha-numerical information from and to the card machines. Card reading and punching rates are 100 to 200 cards per minute, and the line printer rate is 150 lines per minute. Maximum capacity of a card or a printer line is eight computer words, each containing ten decimal digits and sign.

Auxiliary storage of up to four million 11-digit words (ten digits and sign) is provided by magnetic tape units, each with a 400,000-word capacity. A tape-control unit provides the electronic linkage between tape units and the computer. Under the control of the computer each tape unit can search in either direction for address

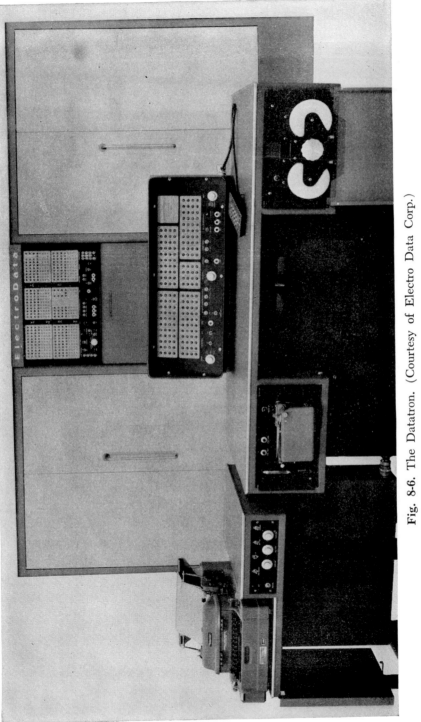

Fig. 8-6. The Datatron. (Courtesy of Electro Data Corp.)

blocks of computer words. Average access time to any word is 192.5 seconds for a random page.

Operating decimally, the computer represents each decimal digit of a number or code instruction by four binary digits in the standard binary coded decimal notation.

The computer uses a one-address order code in which an instruction composed of ten digits occupies the same memory space as a number. The last four digits are the address of a word upon which the command (instruction) will operate, or an indicator specifying some property of the command word. The two middle digits constitute the operation part, while the first four digits are left blank in many instructions, although they may also be used as indicators. For example, the first two digits could indicate either the number of cards to be read or punched, or the number of magnetic tape blocks to be read or written. The third digit indicates which magnetic tape unit is involved in search, and the fourth digit sets the interval for coded automatic stops in the program. An eleventh digit starts or stops paper tape, starts the input, and starts execution after the program has been read in.

Each of the fifty-five arithmetic and logical operations may be carried out as the result of a two-digit instruction. The more complex operations of which the computer is capable are broken down into sequences of these elementary instructions. Sequences used over and over again are prepared only once, stored on paper or magnetic tapes (or punched cards), and are then available as subroutines when required.

The magnetic drum storage has a memory of 4,000 words of eleven digits each. Twenty bands are used on the drum, each of which contains 200 word-positions arranged around the circumference. Each band consists of four tracks. The auxiliary storage is provided by magnetic tape units, each having a capacity of 400,000 words. Electronic linkage between the tape units and the main computer section is by use of a tape control unit.

All operations except multiplication and division are performed in 2 milliseconds per operation, or 500 operations per second. Multiplication requires 8.5 milliseconds, and division 12 milliseconds.

Reference to the main storage system requires 10.5 milliseconds. Random access time to any word in the auxiliary storage is approximately 192 seconds.

ALWAC III-E

The Alwac III-E general-purpose electronic digital computer illustrated in Fig. 8-7 is manufactured by the Alwac Corporation. This computer is of an electronic digital type designed for application to problems of scientific and engineering research, as well as for business, industrial, and financial organizations. The system is able to organize, calculate, and make decisions. It utilizes an internally stored sequence of instructions set up by the operator for application to simple or complex problems. The Alwac can absorb facts in terms of words and numbers, and can store, sort, distribute, rearrange, and call on the information when required for calculation, modification, or output.

The Alwac can store and follow a sequence of up to 16,000 instructions, and by adding, multiplying, subtracting, or dividing, is capable of calculating required answers of any degree of complexity, in any desired sequence. The input and output devices consist of punched paper tape, magnetic tape, punched cards, typewriter keyboard, or high speed reader devices.

As with previously mentioned computers, a Flexowriter can be utilized, plus high speed readers, card converters, and card punchers. A teletype punch operating at 60 characters per second can also be employed.

The Alwac utilizes floating decimal point coding, and the instructions are of the single-address type. A subroutine library is available to owners and users, and consists of a collection of carefully coded and tested routine building blocks which can be assembled by the coder into complex routines.

The magnetic storage drum revolves at 3,500 revolutions per minute with a standard 4,096 word main storage or an optional 8,192 word main storage. The word structure consists of thirty-two bits, plus sign.

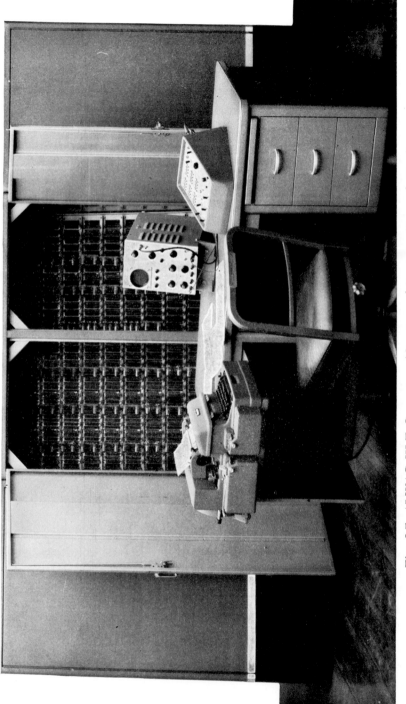

Fig. 8-7. ALWAC III-E Computer. (Courtesy of Logistics Research, Inc.)

Addition or subtraction is performed in 1 to 9 milliseconds, multiplication or division in 17 to 25 milliseconds, and transfers in 1 to 9 milliseconds.

UNIVAC

The Univac II computer, manufactured by the Remington Rand Univac Division of Sperry Rand Corporation, is shown in Fig. 8-8. The supervisory control section, at the left, is the nerve center of the system, giving the operator a continuous picture of the internal operation of the computer. The large unit in the back is the primary and central computer section, containing the calculating circuits. The cabinets at the right handle the magnetic tape which provides high speed input and output for the central computer.

Data to be processed can be put on tape with a Unityper. This is a modified Remington electric typewriter, equipped with electronic circuits to convert the typewritten information into pulse patterns and record them on magnetic tape.

Univac II has a magnetic core memory with a capacity of 24,000 alphabetical or numerical characters, expandable to 120,000 at the user's option.

Auxiliary equipment can be utilized with the Univac, such as a card-to-tape converter which automatically prepares an accurate duplication on tape of the information contained in punched cards. The converter is capable of processing 240 cards per minute. It reads each card twice and compares the second reading with the initial recording which had been placed on the magnetic tape. If the two are not identical, the card is automatically ejected. A tape-to-card converter is also available which furnishes processed results in the form of punched cards at the rate of 120 per minute. A high-speed printer is also available as auxiliary equipment. This unit produces 600 lines per minute on a line 130 characters wide, in any desired format.

The Univac Scientific Model 1103A is shown in Fig. 8-9. This is also a general-purpose digital computer, but this system is designed for applications which require large storage capacities, high operating speeds, and a high degree of programming versatility.

Fig. 8-8. Univac II Computer. (Courtesy of Remington Rand Univac.)

Fig. 8-9. Univac Scientific Model 1103A. (Courtesy of Remington Rand Univac.)

Its high computational speed is secured by use of parallel mode operation, whereby all digits of a number are operated upon simultaneously. Information internally utilizes the binary system and the basic word size consists of thirty-six binary digits or bits. A word may be an instruction, a coded quantity, or a number. The two-address system is employed.

The storage section consists of 16,384 registers of magnetic drum storage and one bank of 4,096 registers of magnetic core storage. (See Chapter 6.) Additional banks of magnetic cores, permitting a total of 12,288 registers, can be included as integral equipment. Supplementary external storage is also provided by one to ten magnetic tape units, each of which is capable of storing 384,000 words in variable block length or continuous mode.

The input-output section of Model 1103A computer is capable of accommodating various types of external equipment, depending on the requirements at a given installation. Input-output buffer registers are employed, which provide communication with external equipment without disturbing arithmetic operations. These registers permit use of several units and allow computation to proceed while external equipment is operating. A feature of this computer is the automatic program interrupt. This provides automatic means for interrupting a program in process by external equipment operating in on-line applications. The program in process is automatically suspended and operation is resumed upon completion of the information exchange with the on-line equipment.

A wide variety of external equipment can be integrated with Univac Scientific operation. Some of these devices are:

High Speed Printer (600 lines per minute and for curve plotting)
Eighty-Column Card-to-Tape Converter
Magnetic-to-Paper Tape Converter
Unityper Magnetic Tape Recorder
Tape-to-Card Converter
Card Reader and Punch
Paper-to-Magnetic Tape Converter
High-Speed Paper-Tape Punch
Uniservo Magnetic-Tape Units
Analog-to-Digital Converter
Transrecorder (remote transmission of data from magnetic tape to magnetic tape)

Electric Typewriter Output
Visual Displays
High-Speed Paper-Tape Reader

Univac Scientific is compatible with other Univac equipment by means of magnetic tape units. Such equipment includes Univac II, Card-to-Tape Converter, Tape-to-Card Converter, and Univac File Computer.

A medium sized electronic computer now being manufactured by Remington Rand Univac, Division of Sperry Rand Corporation, is the Univac File Computer, Fig. 8-10.

Fig. 8-10. Univac File Computer.
(Courtesy of Remington Rand Univac.)

In addition to using the punched card input-output, the File Computer can also use thirty-two other possible input-output units simultaneously. Other units include perforated tape, magnetic tape, line punchers, electric typewriters, key tape printers and key punches.

The philosophy of the Univac File Computer is concentrated in its ability to provide *random access* to tens of thousands of unit records stored on up to ten large-capacity magnetic drums, for a maximum capacity of 1,800,000 characters. This permits the processing of data in the random sequence of its arrival, without waiting for grouping with other data. The data is also available at random, eliminating the need to search records for information. Average access time for processing is 1/3,500 to 1/350 second per value depending upon the size of the unit record.

A few of the many possible applications of the File Computer are inventory control, sales analysis, payroll, purchasing, billing, labor distribution, and production control.

BURROUGHS E-101

The Burroughs Model E-101 digital computer is illustrated in Fig. 8-11. This is a desk size computer designed to solve problems too complex for efficient solution on desk calculators, yet too small for economical solution on the large scale electronic computers.

The input system consists of an eleven-column full keyboard Burroughs bookkeeping machine used in conjunction with program storing pinboards, as described in the previous chapter. The output system is capable of two print-cycles per second (24 digits per second) on rolls or forms up to 18 inches wide. A front feed insert is also provided for single documents, duplicating masters, etc.

Magnetic drum storage is utilized, with either 100 or 220 words having a word length of twelve digits plus sign.

Addition and subtraction are performed at the rate of 20 problems per second, multiplication and division at four problems per second, including access time. The E-101 design permits the computation to be halted at critical steps to permit the operator to choose which of the stages in the calculation is to be handled next.

TRANSAC

The Transac digital computer of the Philco Corporation is a transistorized computer operating on extremely low power and capable of calculations at extremely high speeds. The computer uses a surface barrier transistor which permits 416,000 additions or sub-

Fig. 8-11. Burroughs E-101 Computer. (Courtesy of Burroughs Corp.)

tractions per second. The Transac is capable of multiplying two 6-digit numbers in 48 microseconds, or more than 240,000 times faster than a modern office desk type calculating machine.

The Transac computer utilizes directly coupled circuits (see Chapters 2 and 4). Hence, the size and weight of the Transac units are only about one-third that of conventional transistor circuits.

In the assembly of a computer utilizing the Philco directly coupled circuits, all the calculation and control circuitry are combined on a single replaceable unit—a printed-wiring board or card —having on it only transistors and resistors. No other electronic parts are needed in the arithmetic section. As the precision and versatility of the computer is to be increased, additional cards are added (see Fig. 8-12).

Fig. 8-12. Transac printed boards.
(Courtesy of Philco Corp.)

The control section of the computer uses cards similar in appearance to the "digit" cards except that approximately a half dozen capacitors are also employed. The card units make it possible to assemble these items for the major section of the computer in a minimum of time because of the use of assembled and pretested sections. Input and output systems may be of the conventional type, such as punched cards, electric typewriters, etc.

LGP-30

The LGP-30 illustrated in Fig. 8-13 is a general-purpose digital computer marketed by the Royal McBee Corporation, designed to

Fig. 8-13. The LGP-30 Computer.
(Courtesy of Librascope.)

handle large scale scientific and engineering calculations at high speed. The computer is fully automatic, and is capable of executing programs which require branching or transferring and involve decision characteristics. The command structure for transferring information into the computer is relatively simple, comprising only sixteen orders including the four arithmetical orders.

The Flexowriter, previously discussed, is employed as a combined input-output system. The keyboard of the Flexowriter or its associated tape can be employed for processing the input to the machine.

A magnetic drum memory system is utilized, having a total capacity of 4,096 words. Sixty-four magnetic heads are utilized, each head capable of handling sixty-four words. Each word consists of thirty-two bits. The drum revolves at a speed of approximately 3,600 revolutions per minute, involving a search time per operation of only approximately 2 milliseconds.

Addition can be performed in 0.26 millisecond, multiplication in 17 milliseconds, and division also in 17 milliseconds, the foregoing time factors excluding access time.

The computer contains 113 vacuum tubes and 1,450 germanium diode crystals.

Note: This computer, with panels removed, is illustrated in the next chapter.

BIZMAC

The Bizmac digital computer is a product of the Radio Corporation of America, and is a special-purpose machine especially designed for the Ordnance Tank-Automotive Command, U. S. Army, at Detroit. Its purpose will be electronic stock control of replacement parts for military combat and transport vehicles. The Bizmac performs in minutes inventory control procedures which formerly took months for the army's vast tank-automotive supply program, which involves control and replacement inventories of more than 200,000 different categories of parts.

The unit utilizes magnetic tape, each reel capable of storing 2,500,000 characters. Read and write speeds are at the rate of 10,000 letters or digits per second, operating at a tape speed of 80 inches per second. A high speed printer is utilized (see Chapter 7).

The input device includes a tapewriter which simultaneously produces a punched version, in machine language, on paper tape, plus a typed copy. The unit also contains a tapewriter verifier which verifies the information on the punched tape in order to maintain maximum accuracy. Among the input devices is also a tape transcriber, which transfers the data from the punched tape to magnetic tape at the rate of 12,000 characters per minute. The card transcriber, also utilized, is capable of transferring data from punched cards to magnetic tape with a handling rate of 400 cards per minute.

Questions Relating to Chapter 8

1. Briefly list some of the tasks which can be performed by digital computers.

2. *a*) In the IBM Model 705 computer, describe the input and output devices utilized.
   b) In the Model 705, what are the speeds with which addition, subtraction, and other calculations can be performed?

3. *a*) Briefly explain the purpose and function of the Master Writer in the Bendix G-15 computer.
   b) What type of storage devices are utilized with the G-15 computer?

4. *a*) What type of input devices are utilized with the Readix computer?
   b) What is meant by a block search command with respect to the Readix computer?

5. *a*) Explain the features of the final processor with respect to the Elecom Model 125 computer.
   b) Briefly explain the characteristics of magnetic storage tapes and their access time with respect to the Elecom computer.

6. *a*) Briefly explain the input devices which can be used with the Datatron computer.
   b) What is meant by a one-address order code as used with the Datatron computer?

7. *a*) Briefly explain the general characteristics of the Alwac Model III-E computer.

b) At what speed does the drum rotate in the Alwac, and what is the word storage capacity and the bit capacity of the drum?

8. *a*) Briefly describe the general differences between the Univac II and the Model 1103A.

b) What type of auxiliary equipment can be utilized with the Univac?

9. *a*) Briefly explain the input system employed with the Burroughs Model E-101 computer.

b) Briefly explain how the pinboards are utilized in conjunction with the bookkeeping machine of the Burroughs Model E-101.

10. *a*) List the number per second of the various calculations which can be performed in the Transac computer.

b) What type of circuitry and components is used in the Transac computer?

11. *a*) List the general characteristics of the Librascope LGP-30 computer.

b) Describe the magnetic memory system of the LGP-30.

12. *a*) Briefly describe the general characteristics of the Bizmac computer.

b) Explain the characteristics of the magnetic tape storage devices used with the Bizmac.

9 □ □ □
□ □ □
□ □ ■

Maintenance Factors

In the design of digital computers, manufacturers spare no effort in utilizing tubes, transistors, diodes, and other components which have a great deal of reliability. The usual practice is to operate the various components below the levels at which they are rated by the component manufacturers in order to insure greater reliability and longer life. Since, however, the number of components are so numerous in a digital computer, some maintenance and servicing problems are unavoidable. Regardless of the care taken in the selection and assembly of the various components making up the computer circuitry, some unexpected failures are bound to occur in circuitry which involves thousands of vacuum tubes, germanium diodes, and transistors, as well as component parts consisting of resistors, capacitors, and other such items.

Some computers, as mentioned later in this chapter, have self-checking devices which expedite trouble-shooting and maintenance procedures. Despite self-checking features, however, auxiliary testing equipment is usually required in order to signal-trace the circuits in an effort to localize defective stages. In addition to such testing equipment, the technician concerned with the maintenance

259

and repair of a particular computer must be generally familiar with *that* computer by having studied the manual describing the operational features and general circuitry involved. Such familiarization is essential, because even though all digital computers operate on the basic principles detailed in earlier chapters of this book, important differences exist in the manner in which these circuits are combined to perform the various functions. Differences, of course, also exist in the types of storage systems employed by the distinct computers, as well as in the particular interconnections existing between the racks and panels housing the various computer units.

A familiarization with the general programming procedure involved with any particular computer is also of help during trouble shooting procedures, since random checks can be made of the computing functions of the various circuits as a check against the accuracy of the results obtained. When a check is made which involves procuring the sum of a number of digits in order that such a sum may be tallied against another sum previously obtained, the process is known as a *summation check*. Some computer services manuals contain specific instructions for making a summation check in accordance with the programming procedures necessary for the particular computer. The summation check is invaluable for troubleshooting procedures, because it verifies the accuracy of a computation or calculation. When a summation check is made, the characteristics of the computer with respect to *overflow* and *round-off* must be considered. (Overflow is the condition which occurs when a number of such proportions is produced during the calculation that the number is beyond the capacity of the computer. Round-off relates to the rounding-off of a quantity to the number of significant figures considered expedient.) Both the overflow and round-off limitations of a particular computer should be known to the technician so that test routines can be made well below the normal limitations of the computer.

Troubles may occur in any section of the computer, hence the symptoms which appear when the computer is in operation are of considerable aid in evaluation and isolation of the cause. Troubles arising in the memory section can result in the failure to obtain the stored information. Confining of the trouble to the memory system would be indicated when computations involving stored numbers are inaccurate, while calculations based on information obtained from the accumulators is correct. When accuracy is obtained with computations involving only a few dozen digits but inaccuracy prevails for higher order numbers, the trouble would be indicated as being in the later stages of the accumulators or flip-flop circuits, and hence the necessity for checking all of the various accumulator circuits is eliminated. Troubles in the read-in or print-out circuits can usually be isolated readily in such systems where the calculation processes are indicated on the machine in terms of panel lights or other devices. Trouble with the electric typewriter mechanisms which feed information to the computer or of the punch card mechanisms can be checked without the necessity of feeding information into the computer. Input information can, for instance, be typed on the electric typewriter inputs and the punched tape which results can be compared with the punched tape obtained at an earlier date for an identical input program. Variations in the hole placement of the two tapes would then indicate deviations from normal and correcting procedures could be applied to the input mechanism.

Troubles of a mechanical nature in the electric typewriter itself usually indicate the services of a technician trained in the mechanical aspects of electric typewriter repair, and would not necessarily involve the services of a technician trained in maintenance and trouble shooting aspects of electronic circuitry. Troubles with printers or other read-out devices also usually entail the services of a technician trained in the specialized aspects of the mechanical repairs involved.

The main body of the computer, independent of the read-in and read-out devices, is the concern of the electronic technician with respect to servicing, trouble-shooting, and maintenance. It is in the main body of the computer, in conjunction with whatever storage device is utilized, that there must be employed electronic trouble-shooting practices such as signal tracing, voltage and current measurements, continuity checking, tube, transistor, and crystal diode testing, and the other procedures involved in electronic trouble shooting. This chapter relates to general considerations involved with such maintenance and servicing problems.

TEST EQUIPMENT

The two most useful items for testing procedures of digital computers are the vacuum tube voltmeter and the oscilloscope. The auxiliary devices may consist of a vacuum tube tester as well as a checker for transistors and one for crystal diodes. Often, however, the last component can be checked with respect to the forward and back resistance by use of an ordinary vacuum tube voltmeter, employing the various ohmic ranges available.

The vacuum tube voltmeter is useful for d-c and a-c measurements, and its advantage is that it has an extremely high input impedance and hence does not load down the circuit under test. Thus, the voltage readings obtained from the vacuum tube voltmeter are much more accurate and reliable than the voltage readings which would be obtained with other types of meters. A second choice, if a vacuum tube voltmeter is not available, is the 20,000 ohms per volt voltmeter, which also provides a fairly high input impedance, particularly for the higher scale ranges.

Another important aspect of the vacuum tube voltmeter is its ability to read the ohmic value of resistance from unit values up to 1,000 megohms. This feature permits the direct reading of the ohmic value of resistors, the d-c resistance of coils, and the leakage resistance of paper capacitors, as well as the continuity checking of circuits to ascertain whether or not a short circuit or an open circuit exists. As mentioned earlier, the resistance scales can also be employed to give a quick check of germanium and silicon diodes by reading their forward and back resistance. A rough check can also be made of mica and ceramic capacitors with respect to whether or not they are short circuited, although too much reliance cannot be placed on a reading of leakage resistance except in the case of paper capacitors ranging from 0.002 to some higher value. For mica capacitors having small capacitances, the charging and discharging factors are not noticeable since the small capacitance will not provide much of a needle deflection on the VTVM. With the latter on the highest R scale (R times 1,000 megohms), however, the higher value paper capacitors will indicate their charging rate by the needle deflection from a low value to a high value. If, however, an accurate check must be made of the various capacitors in a computer, a reliable capacitor checker should be employed. Such a capacitor checker should contain provisions for reading the power factor of a capacitor so that an evaluation can be made of the condition of the by-pass and coupling capacitors of the circuitry, as well as the electrolytic filter capacitors of the power supply.

With respect to the type of VTVM desirable for testing and maintenance, one should be employed which utilizes the vacuum tube principle with respect to the *a-c measurements* as well as the *d-c measurements*. Some lower priced VTVM models utilize the vacuum tube voltmeter principle only on the d-c scale.

The ordinary VTVM is usually calibrated to read the effective value of voltage (0.707 times the peak value), but a desirable feature available in the more expensive types is the ability to read peak-to-peak voltages. This feature will provide a means for checking low frequency pulse components, though for the higher frequency pulses with extremely short durations and sharp rise times it is advisable to utilize an oscilloscope which has the required sensitivity to provide faithful reproduction of the microsecond pulses employed in computers.

The oscilloscope is an indispenable instrument for the maintenance and servicing of digital computers because it provides a means for visual observation of the various pulse signals encountered in the circuits. With a good oscilloscope, the waveshape of the pulse can be studied and evaluated in terms of distortion, rise time, etc. A properly calibrated oscilloscope is also useful for an accurate measurement of the peak amplitude of a particular pulse.

The requirements with respect to an oscilloscope are more severe than for such an instrument used in television servicing, because of the short duration pulses employed in digital computers. With pulses having durations in the order of 1 or 2 microseconds, a faithful reproduction of the pulse waveform necessitates that the vertical amplifier circuitry of the oscilloscope have wideband characteristics to accommodate the necessary harmonic components of the pulse. If there is any attenuation of the higher frequency components of the pulse under observation, it will result in pulse distortion. Since such pulse distortion would be contributed by the oscilloscope, it might be erroneously assumed that such distortion is caused by the computer circuitry and in consequence incorrect diagnoses would be made.

The vertical *sensitivity* is also an important factor, since low amplitude pulses cannot be expanded to full screen size when the necessity for such expansion arises. Thus, the vertical amplifier of the oscilloscope must be able to accommodate a wide band of frequencies such as would be encountered for the various pulses of the computer, and its sensitivity must be of a high order so that the low amplitude signals can be viewed with the same dimensions as the higher amplitude ones.

The horizontal sweep oscillator of the oscilloscope should also be capable of providing various horizontal sweep frequencies so that one or more pulses can be observed on the screen as desired. Synchronization circuits and other circuits of the oscilloscope should be sufficiently stable so that the pulses under observation can be held at a steady-state condition on the screen.

The oscilloscope can, of course, be dispensed with in such cases where a high quality oscilloscope has already been built into the computer and forms an integral part of its circuitry. In such an instance, all the required signal observations and measurements can be made by switching the oscilloscope to the various circuits where tests are to be made, as more fully described later for typical commercial models.

TRANSISTORS AND TUBES

Transistors, vacuum tubes, and crystal diodes are usually operated considerably below their ratings in order to assure long life. In general, vacuum tubes have an average life of 5,000 hours, though some special-purpose vacuum tubes have been designed to have an average life of 10,000 hours. In computer use, however, where the tubes are operated at only 70 per cent or less of their rated power, tube life will be extended to a considerable degree. Transistors, on the other hand, have an average life estimated at 90,000 hours and again, if operated below their normal ratings, should have an indefinite computer life.

Vacuum tubes and transistors operating in bistable devices such as the Eccles-Jordan flip-flop circuits, will often operate satisfactorily when their characteristics such as transconductance and mu have changed to some extent. A change of the operating characteristics of a vacuum tube may be a detriment when such a tube is used as an audio amplifier. For instance, such a change would not affect its operation in a flip-flop circuit because the tube operates only at saturation or at cut-off, hence a change in its characteristics would not be significant. If, however, a tube becomes gassy it will draw considerably more current during the saturation cycle than would otherwise be the case, and such an excessive current flow can damage resistors, transformers, or other component parts associated with the computer system. Thus, if resistor No. R4 shown in Fig. 9-1 is burned out, the tube should be checked to ascertain whether or not it is gassy and has caused the burnout.

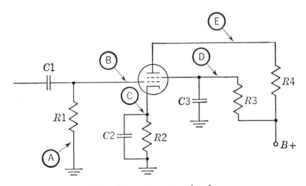

Fig. 9-1. Circuit checks.

Tubes, transistors, and crystal diodes, of course, may not always be at fault when circuit troubles occur, though it is a good practice to check such items first before proceeding with extensive checks of component parts. If, however, a tube check for a circuit such as shown in Fig. 9-1 fails to disclose trouble, then other items must be tested. The check points shown in the circles marked A, B, etc. are useful for trouble isolation. A voltage reading between B and C, for instance, should indicate a negative polarity at the grid, since current flow through R2 makes the cathode more positive than the grid. Zero voltage, or a positive potential between B and C, indicates a check for leakage of capacitor $C1$, or for a short circuited $C2$ capacitor or $R2$ resistor.

A voltage reading between B and A should show zero voltage, or a small residual d-c voltage during signal input. A plus voltage may indicate a gassy tube or a leakage in $C1$ permitting some plus potential to leak across $C1$ from the previous stage. A reading between C and A should show a plus potential because of the current flow through $R2$. Zero voltage indicates either a short circuited $C2$ or $R2$. An open $R2$ would also cause a zero voltage reading between C and A, though with a sensitive VTVM the plus voltage through the high tube resistance may still be in evidence.

If capacitor $C3$ short circuits, there will be zero reading between D and A, and resistor $R3$ will become excessively hot or may burn out. Thus, a burned-out $R3$ calls for a check of $C3$.

As mentioned earlier, a gassy tube can cause a burnout of $R4$, or cause the resistor to heat excessively. In the latter instance there will be excessive current through $R4$ and the voltage between E and A will be below normal. With $R4$ burned out, no voltage reading will be obtained between E and A.

If a check of component parts fails to disclose the trouble, then a recheck should be made of the tubes. Vacuum tubes should be tested with a good tube checker, preferably of the transconductance type which will also give an indication of abnormal current flow. Transistors, also, should be checked in a transistor tester which is capable of indicating the various faults which develop in a transistor, such as a burned-out emitter-base section, an abnormally low resistance path through the emitter or collector side, or insufficient alpha or beta current differentials between input and output circuits.

Transistors which plug into miniature sockets present no particular problems in installation, except that care should be taken to make sure the lead wires are properly spaced and that the transistor is not inserted in the socket in a reversed lead sequence position. With transistors which require soldering into the circuit, however, precautions must be observed. Transistors can be damaged readily by absorbing excessive heat through lead terminals from a soldering iron. For this reason it is preferable to have both the leads from a transistor and the circuit wiring to which the transistor is to be attached well cleaned before the soldering process. Wires should be scraped clean with a knife, and a well tinned soldering iron should be utilized so that the soldering process can be expedited quickly. A prolonged soldering process usually causes transistor damage. A good idea is to grip the transistor lead which is to be soldered with the ends of thin-nose pliers as shown in Fig. 9-2, as

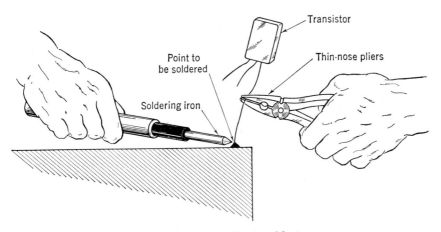

Fig. 9-2. Transistor lead soldering.

an aid toward absorbing excessive heat by the pliers instead of the transistor. A low wattage soldering iron is recommended, and the soldering process should be completed in as short a time as possible to keep the heat application time at a minimum.

PRINTED WIRING FACTORS

When it is necessary to solder component parts to printed wire circuitry, special precautions must also be observed since the techniques differ from circuits which employ interconnecting wires between the various components. The printed circuit wiring consists only of an extremely thin layer of conductive material photoetched on a plastic or other nonconducting base, and heat from a soldering iron can often melt the etched conductive surface.

Where the printed wiring is in the form of an extremely thin copper strip, the damaged resistor or capacitor can be clipped off the printed wiring section by using diagonal cutters so as not to tear or break the printed wiring. A sharp pen knife can then be inserted under the end of the printed wiring section as shown in Fig. 9-3,

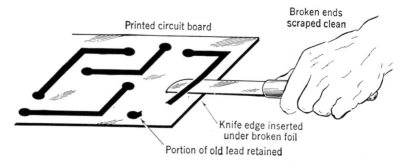

Fig. 9-3. Printed circuit repair.

lifting it. Both sides of the printed wire strip are carefully scraped with the pen knife, and then tinned using a low wattage soldering iron. The leads from the resistor or capacitor are also tinned prior to the joining of the printed wiring strip and the resistor. The soldering process, as in the case with transistors, should be rapid so that a minimum of heat is applied. After the soldered joints have cooled, the loose ends can be taped down with electrical tape, or plastic cement applied to the sections. The sections can be weighted down temporarily until the plastic cement hardens to form a rigid replacement.

If the printed wiring is particularly thin and of the etched variety where the strip cannot be lifted, an attempt will have to be made to solder the replacement component to a portion of the lead which was left when the old component was cut away.

Many printed circuit sections are of an individual type, and when any part of the printed circuit is damaged the entire section can be replaced without requiring an attempt to repair the damaged component. An inspection of the particular defective component and area will disclose whether the entire unit is replaceable or only the component part can be replaced.

Often printed circuits are coated with a silicone resin varnish or clear lacquer to minimize the effects of humidity. When repairs are made to such printed circuits, the repaired area should be re-coated with lacquer to reseal it against moisture.

When components are removed from a printed circuit board care should be taken to prevent breakage along the copper foil path. If breakage does occur, it can usually be jumped by a drop of solder. If a break has an appreciable gap, it may be necessary to use regular hookup wire to jump the gap.

Some printed wiring boards have a degree of flexibility which endangers the copper foil etchings if the board is subjected to undue stress. Hence, undue pressure should be avoided and the entire section inspected carefully after a repair has been made.

MAINTENANCE FACTORS

Often plug-in units contain an entire computing section, and if trouble occurs in one of these sections a replacement section can be utilized while the damaged one is under repair. A typical item of this type is the Transac arithmetic control unit developed by the Philco Corporation, as more fully discussed previously. The unit contains almost a thousand transistors, 300 resistors, and twelve capacitors which are permanently dip-soldered into the compact printed circuit plug-in cards. Maintenance procedures are simplified if extra units are on hand for replacement purposes when troubles develop in a particular unit.

Maintenance is facilitated by the degree with which the manufacturer makes available test panels and racks. In the Bendix G-15 computer, a power panel is provided as shown in Fig. 9-4(A). This panel contains all meters and switches necessary for the adjustments and control of power to the computer. The computer is turned on and off at this section and voltage levels within the computer may be ascertained directly from the panel. Adjustable dials provide for changing voltages within limits in order to make marginal checks on the computer operation. *Marginal checks* in a computer relate to the procedure of increasing or decreasing voltages on a stage, or a succession of stages, to localize defects. A weak tube, for instance, may function on the border line, or may even behave in intermittent fashion on occasion. During checking procedures, however, the tube

Fig. 9-4(A). Bendix G-15 power panel.
(Courtesy of Bendix Corp.)

may appear to be operating normally. With a marginal check of decreased voltage, however, the weak tube may become totally inoperative while the good tubes will still function. Thus, the borderline or intermittent tube can be found. A marginal check can also, in the case of intermittent operation, increase the frequency of the intermittent condition to a sufficient degree where circuit or tube localization is possible. By marginal checks during periodic maintenance procedures it is also possible to anticipate failure of a weak component or tube, and correct the condition before trouble occurs. This minimizes the danger of several weak circuits going bad at one time and aggravating trouble-shooting problems.

On the Bendix power panel shown in Fig. 9-4(A) a *running time* meter is also included, which indicates the accumulated operating hours so that a check may be made of the total time the computer has been in operation. With this type of meter, regularly scheduled maintenance checks can be made for every 250, 500, or 1,000 hours of operation, as desired.

The running time meter is at the upper left of the panel while the a-c voltmeter is at the upper right. The center meter indicates the percentage of d-c voltage. The lower knobs are for the marginal voltage checks and for clearing the computer.

The Bendix computer also contains a neon lamp instruction (command) indicator panel as shown in Fig. 9-4(B), which permits the stopping of the computer at selected points in the program routine in order to check the operations up to the selected point. The command indicator panel is used to indicate the last executed command instruction at the time that the computer has been stopped. This indication is displayed by neon bulbs which show the source, the destination, the transfer characteristics, the line from which the instruction was read, the present status of the input and output systems, and other appropriate information relative to the execution of the instructions. During the time the computer is involved in the processes of calculations, the neon displays change very rapidly. The command indicator panel, however, is useful even during the computing processes because it will indicate whether or not the computer is going through normal operational procedures.

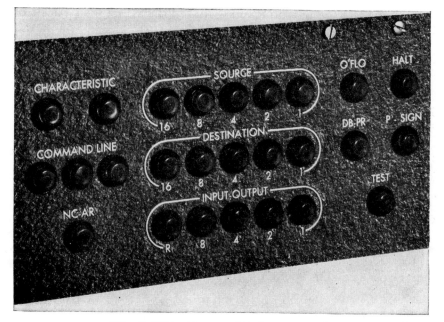

Fig. 9-4(B). Command indicator panel.
(Courtesy of Bendix Corp.)

GENERAL FACTORS

Maintenance and servicing of digital computers are not overly difficult tasks for the technician who has a general knowledge of the fundamental aspects of digital computers and has the ability to perform the various servicing routines of voltage, current, and resistance measurements, tube and transistor checking, and signal tracing. When difficulty in any particular circuit has been localized, a knowledge of the manner in which such a circuit should behave and perform will expedite the repair of that circuit. If the computer programming is not too complex, a knowledge of the procedures involved is also an aid to the maintenance or servicing technician. If the technician has the ability to inject simple calculating routines or specific test routines into the computer, he can evaluate the results which should be obtained from such calculations and can thus ascertain the performance status of the computer and isolate the defective circuits and component parts. Since, however, the various computers on the market differ from one another in the manner in which the programs are established, the technician must become familiar with the particular programming factors involved in the computer to be serviced. Also, since the physical arrangement of the various circuits differs for the various computers it is necessary to consult the descriptive literature or service notes which accompany a particular computer. If the service notes are particularly thorough, many hints and suggestions will be given for servicing and testing routines which will help expedite the trouble-shooting procedures. A technician having a fairly good groundwork in the fundamentals of digital computers soon becomes adept at trouble-shooting and maintenance when his work is confined to a particular computer.

Most computers are so designed that maintenance and servicing problems are held at a minimum by the ready accessibility of the various tubes or transistors utilized as well as identification or labeling of the circuits employed. A typical example of this is the Royal McBee LGP-30 computer. This computer employs 113 vacuum tubes and 1,450 diodes, and operates on 115 volts a-c, 1.5 kilowatts.

As shown earlier in Fig. 8-13 (and in Fig. 9-5 with front panel of the computer removed), the Flexowriter previously discussed is employed in conjunction with the computer and the complete general purpose computer has been designed to occupy a small space as compared with some other types. Plug-in units with printed circuits are used throughout the computer, including the logical section for simplification of maintenance and servicing procedures. As with many other computers, each electronic component is operated well below its normal rating for additional life and reliability.

Besides the Flexowriter, the operator also utilizes the control panel at the upper left-hand section of the computer next to the Flexowriter. An oscilloscope tube is used to display the contents of the sequence control register, the instruction register, and the accumulator. As with most devices which contain a number of component parts, it is preferable for the unit to come up to proper operating temperature before the computation process is begun. Positioning the *operate* switch starts the computer, and while the machine is warming up a light indicating "stand by to operate" is

Fig. 9-5. LGP-30 Computer with panels removed. (Courtesy of Librascope.)

turned on. When the machine has warmed up, a light under the operate button comes on and the computer is then ready to use. A *stand-by* button is provided which shuts off all power except that to the tube filaments, which receive only half power. This feature allows the machine to be in readiness for operation and saves power and wear until ready for use.

In the normal operating mode, the start button causes the computer to execute the instructions of the program in the memory. During servicing or maintenance, however, the "one operation" switch is utilized and the start button then causes the machine to execute only one instruction of the program. The computer stops after executing one instruction, thus making it possible to go through an entire program step by step to observe the result of each operation on the oscilloscope.

As with all devices using a number of vacuum tubes, the unit is cooled by an internal forced-air blower. The air filter is shown at the bottom right of Fig. 9-5 and at the lower left of Fig. 9-6. In the latter illustration, the rear panels have also been removed to expose the various units. In actual operation, only the pushbutton control panel adjacent to the Flexowriter is accessible.

The cooling unit is at the lower left of Fig. 9-5 and the digital display unit is below the control panel and above the cooling unit. The adjusting controls for the oscilloscope display tube are accessible on the panel on the front of the digital display unit, and permit adjustments of the intensity, focus, vertical gain, etc. of the oscilloscope screen. The unit at the upper right contains the magnetic drum which operates at a speed of 3,600 rpm and has a capacity of 4,096 words.

At the left of Fig. 9-6 are the plug-in units, each containing four vacuum tubes and other component parts. This section contains the various flip-flop circuits, matrix circuits, read and record circuits, and amplifier circuits.

At the lower right-hand section of the unit (Fig. 9-6) is the power sequence control unit, and above this unit are the plug-in circuits consisting of additional flip-flops, converter stages, etc. All the plug-in units are labeled for easy identification and maintenance procedures. The oscilloscope tube is shown at the top of the computer at the rear.

Fig. 9-6. Rear panels removed in LGP-30. (Courtesy of Librascope.)

276

Questions Relating to Chapter 9

1. Explain what features vacuum tube voltmeters and oscilloscopes should have for expediting trouble-shooting of digital computer circuits.

2. *a*) Generally, are tubes, transistors, and component parts operated at 50, 75, or 100 per cent of their ratings?
b) Compare the average life of vacuum tubes with that of transistors, and explain why slight changes of characteristics are not so important in computers as in amplifiers handling audio of radio-frequency signals.

3. If a burned-out resistor is found in a circuit, what procedures should be undertaken in addition to replacement of the resistor?

4. What effects will a gassy tube have on a circuit?

5. List some of the precautions necessary when replacing transistors in computer circuitry.

6. What factors and precautions relate to printed wiring repairs?

7. Briefly explain what is meant by *marginal checks*, and also indicate their usefulness in maintenance work.

8. Why is it important for a maintenance or servicing technician to understand the programming procedures in the computer he services?

9. What advantages are there to a "one operation" process in a computer?

Glossary

Abacus ... An elementary form of a digital computer consisting of a framework with movable beads or balls strung on rods.

Access Time ... The time interval between the calling for information from a computer unit and the instant that such information is delivered.

Accumulator ... A computer unit wherein numbers are accumulated. Usually an accumulator holds one number in storage, and when a second number is entered the accumulator adds the two numbers and retains in storage the sum.

Accuracy ... The degree by which a solution is correct or free of error.

Adder ... An electronic circuit capable of providing the sum of two numbers entered therein.

Address ... An identifying number or numbers, or a particular group of symbols which identifies the location of a particular storage location.

Alphabetical Coding ... A system whereby abbreviations in alphabetical form are employed for preparation of computer programming.

Alpha-Numerical ... Relating to abbreviating systems employed for programming purposes wherein alphabetical as well as numerical designations are employed.

Analog ... Having to do with calculations involving physical variables which correspond with numerical variables.

Analog Computer ... A computer which handles calculations by utilizing physical analogs of such variables.

And-Circuit ... A gating circuit having two or more inputs, providing an output only if all of the input terminals receive pulses. Upon the application of pulses to some (but not all) input lines, no output pulses are produced.

Arabic Numbers ... Numbers employing Arabic symbols and comprising our present-day symbols between 0 and 9.

Arithmetic Check ... Checking a calculation by employing arithmetical rules, as testing a division such as $A/B = C$ by multiplying B by C and comparing the answers.

279

Attenuation ... Diminishing or reducing the amplitude of pulses or other signals.

Automation ... Production by devices or machines which are self-acting with respect to predetermined processes, performing such processes automatically. Automation includes the automatic fabrication by machines of products in a manner previously determined by a particular program.

Auxiliary Storage ... (See *Secondary Storage*.)

Base ... In relation to numbers, the unit employed for construction of arithmetic tables. In decimal notation, the base is ten; in binary notation, the base is two. (See *Radix*.)

B-H Curve ... A graph of the magnetizing force required for the flux density produced. A curve of magnetic characteristics.

Bias ... The negative potential applied to a vacuum tube; or in a transistor, voltage employed for establishing an operating point for the signal information.

Binary ... Involving two symbol units such as 0 and 1.

Binary-Coded Decimal Notation ... A system whereby each decimal digit of a number is assigned a symbol made up of binary digits.

Binary Digit ... A single unit in binary notation. The digit consists of either 0 or 1, and is related to the state of a circuit with respect to an "off" or "on" condition.

Binary Notation ... A system where the numbering involves the base two, utilizing the digits 0 and 1.

Binary Point ... The point in binary notation which is comparable to the decimal point in a decimal number.

Binary-to-Decimal Conversion ... The converting of a binary (base two) number to the equivalent decimal (base ten) number.

Bistable ... Having two stable states such as nonconduction and saturation.

Bit ... A single binary digit. A single pulse in a computer.

Boolean Algebra ... A system employing a special algebra having particular value in design of switching circuits.

Breakpoint ... With reference to computer programming, a particular point in a program routine wherein the operation of the computer is interrupted for the purposes of a check of the status of the instructions being performed.

Capacity ... With respect to computers, the limit of bits or characters which can be handled by the computer.

Card Reader ... In relation to punch card machines, a device which interprets the information stored on cards by passing them over sensing devices.

Cascade . . . In vacuum tubes, a circuit where the anode output is coupled to the grid circuit of the succeeding stage. In transistors, coupling from collector to base. Both are conventional forms.

Cascode . . . In vacuum tubes, a circuit where the output of the anode is applied to the cathode of a subsequent stage. In transistors, from collector to emitter.

Cathode Follower . . . A circuit so designed that the cathode signal "follows" the phase of the input signal. The circuit functions as an impedance step-down device.

Character . . . In computers, a single symbol such as a decimal digit from 0 to 9, a letter, or any other type of single symbol which may be involved in the storage, reading-in, or reading-out processes.

Clearing Pulse . . . A pulse which is employed for clearing or resetting a circuit to its previous state.

Clipper . . . A circuit which clips the peaks from pulses or other signal waveforms.

Coded Decimal . . . A type of notation in which each decimal digit is identified by a group of binary ones and zeros (usually in groups of four, such as 0010 for 2).

Coincidence Circuit . . . A circuit which must have inputs which coincide to produce an output. An *and*-circuit.

Comparator . . . A circuit used for making a comparison between two numbers or signals for the purpose of establishing whether there is agreement or disagreement between the two, and providing an indicating signal to denote which is the case.

Complement . . . A mathematical process employed in computers involving derived quantities for use in checking computations.

Conditional . . . A process or routine which is influenced by the results of a comparison made between two conditions during the calculation process. Conditional may also make a process subject to control by the operator.

Conditional Breakpoint Instruction . . . In programming, a conditional instruction which, at a predetermined time, will stop the computing process to permit the entry of instructions for continuing along the same routine or to another routine.

Conditional Transfer . . . An instruction of the program which causes the computer to do either of the following: transfer to another indicated instruction or continue with the next instruction, according to the status of the computation as determined at that point.

Control Circuits . . . Those circuits in a computer which are involved with the carrying out of the program instructions.

Control Register . . . The computer unit which contains in storage the specific instruction relating to the computer processes involved for an operating cycle.

Converter . . . A device for changing data of one type suitable for a particular circuit or machine into corresponding data of another kind for another device. As an example, the device which relates the information stored on punched cards into data suitable for storage in a magnetic drum is a converter.

Counter . . . A unit of the computer which produces the sums of digital numbers, or indicates totals of numbers entered.

Cryotron . . . A device operated at near zero temperature so that large current changes can be obtained by relatively small magnetic field changes.

Cut-off . . . The condition in a tube or transistor wherein current flow no longer occurs.

Cybernetics . . . The study of electrical or electromechanical logic systems including analog or digital computers.

Data Processing Computer . . . A digital computer so designed that it lends itself to the compiling, tabulating, and otherwise processing commercial data and storing (internal filing) of same.

Decade Counters . . . In digital computers, an electronic counter which automatically resets to zero at the count of ten.

Decimal Notation . . . A numbering system concerned with the scale of ten (base ten) using symbols from 0 to 9.

Decimal-to-Binary Conversion . . . Changing a number written in the scale of ten into its equivalent number in the scale of two system.

Delay Line . . . A circuit, mercury column, or other device employed for the purpose of delaying a pulse or pulses for a prescribed time.

Differentiating Circuit . . . A circuit which modifies a pulse or square wave by retaining the high frequency components of the signal and attenuating the lower frequency components.

Digit . . . A single number such as 0 or 1, used in any numbering system such as scale of ten, scale of two, etc.

Digital . . . Relating to numbers expressed in digits.

Digital Computer . . . A type of computer in which digits are used to indicate or represent numbers or quantities.

Discharge Circuit . . . A sawtooth-forming circuit.

Divider . . . A circuit composed of shift registers, subtracters, or scalers for the purposes of electronic division in digital computers.

Drum . . . A cylinder coated with material capable of being magnetized so that it can be employed for the retention of information for storage purposes.

Dynamic Storage ... A storage system in which the information changes with respect to time, such as the mercury column delay line.

Eccles-Jordan ... The last names of W. H. Eccles and F. W. Jordan, the originators of the flip-flop bistable circuit which bears their names.

Excess-Three Code ... A notation similar to pure binary notation, except that each number is represented as a binary number plus three.

Ferrite ... A hard and brittle crystal material made from a mixture of magnetic metals.

Ferrite Ring ... A tiny ring with a high permeability utilized for magnetic storage.

Ferrite Toroid ... (See *Ferrite Ring.*)

Flip-Flop ... A bistable circuit which can be changed from one stable state to another by the insertion of a signal pulse.

Floating-Point Calculation ... A type of calculation used to save time by expressing numbers exponentially.

Flywheel Effect ... The interchange of electric energy between the capacitance and inductance forming a resonant circuit.

Four-Address ... With respect to computer programming, the process of having each complete instruction indicate the addresses of the operations, as well as the operations to be performed, and the location of the storage for the results of the operation, as well as the address of the next instruction. Hence, the four-address instructions involve a particular arithmetic operation.

Full-Adder ... An adder circuit which can complete the adding procedure involving the carry process as distinguished from the half-adder which is incapable of transferring the carry.

Gate ... An electronic circuit in which signals applied to one input are permitted to enter the circuit and provide an output only upon the application of signals to the second input; for example, an and-gate, which is a gating-in device. An inhibitory circuit is also a gating device because the inhibitory signals applied to the second input will gate out any signals applied to the first input line.

General-Purpose Computer ... The type of computer which is capable of handling a variety of problems.

Half-Adder ... A partial adding circuit which must be combined with another half-adder and a circuit capable of performing the carry function to form a full-adder.

Hysteresis ... The lagging of the flux density behind the magnetizing force.

Hysteresis Loop ... A graph or curve of the magnetic characteristics of a substance.

Inhibitory Pulse ... A pulse which acts to inhibit or suppress another signal from going through a circuit and appearing at the output.

Instruction ... In programming, a set of identifying characters or a computer "word" which is designed to cause the computer to perform specific operations.

Integer ... A whole number.

Integrating Circuit ... A circuit which modifies a signal by attenuating the high frequency components of a pulse or square wave while retaining low frequency components.

Latency ... A word sometimes used to indicate the delay encountered in obtaining information from storage.

Leading Edge ... The initial amplitude change of a pulse. The rising amplitude portion of a positive pulse, or the falling amplitude portion of a negative pulse.

Limiter ... A circuit which holds a signal waveform within prescribed amplitude limits.

Magnetic Drum ... A cylinder coated with magnetic material which is used for the storage of information by magnetizing certain areas during rotation of the cylinder.

Marginal Checking ... A test of the borderline operating factors of a unit; for example, lowering the heater voltages of vacuum tubes and then testing the associated circuits to ascertain whether or not they still operate satisfactorily under the reduced heater potentials.

Master Clock ... The timed and synchronized generators which comprise the source of the computer signals.

Mathematical Check ... A test of a calculation by employing mathematical processes, such as checking the results of multiplication by employing division, etc.

Matrix ... A word based on the mathematical process of forming numbers in rectangular or square formations and hence referring to an assembly of components for mixing, storing, or combining signal information by assembling such components in matrix fashion.

Memory ... A word sometimes used to indicate the storage properties of a computer.

Mercury Column ... A tube of mercury utilized to delay sonic frequency signals in a mercury storage device.

Multiplier ... In digital computers, a combination of circuits which performs the functions of multiplication.

Multivibrator ... An *RC* oscillator using two tubes (or two transistors) which operate alternately at conduction and saturation, and hence produce a continuous output signal.

Notation ... A system for number representation, such as decimal notation or binary notation.

Not-Circuit ... A circuit in which the output signal does not have the same phase as the input signal. A phase inverter.

Numerical Coding ... A system using numbers for identification of specific information, as opposed to alphabetical coding.

Oersted ... A unit of magnetizing force.

One-Address (also called single-address) ... In programming, an instruction which contains only a single stage location and the operation to be performed.

One-Shot Multivibrator ... A multivibrator which changes state for a short duration upon the application of an input pulse and then reverts back to its original state automatically.

Operation Code ... In programming, that part of an instruction which indicates the particular mathematical operation which is to be performed.

Or-Circuit ... A circuit having two or more inputs which will provide an output pulse whenever a pulse is applied to either or both of the inputs.

Overflow ... The condition which occurs when a number of such proportions is produced that it is beyond the capacity that the computer can handle.

Parallel Mode ... A group of numbers or other symbols handled simultaneously.

Parity Check ... The process of carrying along a digit for use as a check operation. The digit is called a parity digit and is 1 if the sum of the ones in the computer is odd, and 0 if the sum of the ones is even.

Place ... The numerical designation given to the position of the digits of a number, starting from the right and progressing to the left. In the number 23, the 3 is in first place and the 2 is in second place.

Plugboard ... In programming, a board containing electric terminals which are connected to plugs. Rods or cores are inserted into the plugs in a prescribed manner dictated by the information to be conveyed to the computer.

Precise ... The indication of how close a number is to the actual value. Precision is related to the number of significant figures present.

Program ... A complete set of word instructions indicating the sequential order which the computer must follow for solving a particular problem.

Program Register ... Another term for the control register which stores a given set of instructions of a program and has control of the operation of the computer for the execution of the stored information.

Pulse ... A waveform having either a negative or a positive polarity and starting at a zero reference level. It has a sharp rise and decline time, with an appreciable interval of maximum amplitude.

Pulse Code ... A series of pulses which are identified with a particular meaning.

Quartz Crystal ... A piezoelectric crystal which has the property of converting sound waves to electric pulses and vice versa.

Radix ... The basic number in a particular numbering system. For instance, 10 is the radix for the decimal system, and 2 the radix of the binary system.

Random Access ... A condition where access to the storage system of a computer and the read-out of information therefrom is made by random choice.

Read ... The process of transferring information from one storage device to another, or obtaining from external storage such as punched cards or tape the information for application to internal computer circuitry. Any process of extracting stored information.

Read-in ... To insert information obtained from punched cards or other external storage devices into a computer.

Read-Out ... To bring out of the computer storage information held therein.

Regenerate ... To revitalize or restore to acceptable proportions information held in storage devices where the information deteriorates over a short period of time.

Register ... The word used to designate a specific computer unit which stores one computer word.

Relaxation Oscillator ... An *RC* oscillator of the multivibrator type.

Relay Driver ... A high-current circuit suitable for relay tripping.

Repetition Rate ... The number of times a pulse or signal is received during a given time interval.

Reset ... To cause a flip-flop stage or register to revert to its zero state or to some other condition it held initially.

Residual Magnetism ... The remaining magnetism after the magnetizing force has been removed.

Rise Time ... The time interval required for the leading edge of a pulse to reach its maximum amplitude.

Round-Off ... The rounding off of a quantity to the number of significant figures considered expedient. Round-off alters a precise quantity to one less precise but still serving a useful or satisfactory purpose.

Round-Off Errors ... Errors which accumulate during the solving of a problem or during a calculation process due to the rounding off process applied to successive numbers.

Routine ... A sequence of operations or instructions relating to the operations which a computer is to perform as part of a programming procedure.

Saturation ... The condition in a tube or transistor wherein a maximum current is flowing for the characteristics of the circuit involved and the voltage applied thereto.

Sawtooth ... A waveform having a gradual rise time and an abrupt decline.

Scaler ... A computer circuit which provides lower numerical outputs for a given input number.

Secondary Storage ... A term sometimes applied to storage devices which are not part of the computer circuitry itself, but may be under the control of the computer by direct hookup. Typical examples are: plug boards, magnetic tapes, and ferrite core matrices. Also known as auxiliary storage.

Sense Wire ... A read-out wire which links all of the ferrite cores in a storage matrix.

Serial Operation ... In contrast to parallel mode operation, serial operation consists of a sequential order of binary numbers or other signal information with respect to its application to a computer circuit or its routine therein.

Shift Register ... A circuit which will shift a digit or a group of digits either to the left or to the right, and is of particular importance in some multiplication and division processes.

Sinewave ... A waveform having successive alternations of opposite polarity. Rise time and decline time of each alternation is gradual with a minimum interval of maximum amplitude. In its pure state it represents a single fundamental frequency.

Single-Address ... (See *One-Address*.)

Sonic Delay Line ... A delay line employing a medium such as mercury through which sonic impulses travel in a given time interval, such sonic impulses having been converted from electric impulses.

Sonic Storage ... A storage device which employs a sonic delay line for the storage process.

Special-Purpose Computer ... A computer designed to handle a particular task as opposed to a general-purpose type computer.

Square Wave ... A continuous waveform having one alternation positive and the other negative. Each alternation has a sharp rise and decline time, with an appreciable interval of maximum amplitude.

Start-Stop Multivibrator ... An *RC* oscillator wherein the output waveform duration is controlled by a starting pulse and a stopping pulse.

Static Storage ... A storage device wherein the information is of a fixed nature and is retained while the power is on. Typical examples include the electrostatic storage, and the flip-flop stage.

Storage Drum ... A cylinder coated with magnetic material utilized for magnetic storage.

Storage Register ... A register in the storage system of a computer as contrasted with other computer registers not associated with the storage system.

Subroutine ... A special sequence of instructions which involve a particular mathematical or logical operation which is not an inherent operation of the machine. A subroutine may consist of the instructional steps necessary for solving square roots, logarithms, etc. as opposed to basic arithmetic operations of multiplication, addition, etc.

Subtracter ... A circuit combination which performs the functions of electronic subtraction in a digital computer.

Summation Check ... A check which involves procuring the sum of a number of digits in order that such a sum may be tallied against another sum previously obtained. The summation check is used to verify the accuracy of a computation or a calculation, and is usually made without regard for any possible overflow.

Superconductivity ... The absence of resistance exhibited by certain materials when subjected to near zero temperatures.

Symbolic Logic ... Applying reasoning processes to calculations by using symbols that expedite the procedures. Nonnumerical relationships are usually involved, and a branch of symbolic logic is Boolean algebra. That system is of material aid in applying logical design procedures to computer circuitry.

Test Routine ... A sequence of operations employed for checking a computer with respect to proper function.

Three-Address ... A system whereby an instruction contains two operand addresses, and the address of the next instruction as well as its operation.

Thyratron ... A gas filled tube having a control grid.

Trailing Edge ... The amplitude decline edge of a positive pulse or the amplitude rise edge of a negative pulse.

Transistor ... A germanium or silicon crystal semiconductor device which exhibits the amplifying and signal-generating characteristics of a vacuum tube.

Trigger Circuit ... A bistable circuit which can be triggered by an input pulse to change it from one stable state to another.

Truncate ... Sometimes used to refer to the process of dropping several digits of a number. A round-off process.

Two-Address ... The term used to indicate the type of instruction that includes two addresses as well as specifying an operation.

Unconditional Transfer ... An instruction which interrupts an orderly sequence of procedures and permits the next instruction to be obtained from an address (storage location) other than that which would normally follow in the sequence of procedures.

Williams' Tube ... An electrostatic storage tube employing the cathode ray principle, designed by F. C. Williams.

Word ... A particular number of characters handled as a unit by the computer and having a specific meaning with respect to the computation process.

Resistor and Capacitor Color Codes

Since the advent of radio several decades ago, there has been a large variety of resistors and capacitors manufactured. In the early days there was a considerable difference in appearance between resistors and capacitors. In color coding the resistor so that the value of the resistor in ohms could be ascertained from the colors presented, the body of the resistor was painted a particular color, and additional colors were used at each end to provide two significant figures and the multiplier. The mica capacitors were stamped with dots of color, which was a convenient procedure since the capacitors were flat. Eventually, however, molded tubular and ceramic capacitors appeared which had a shape similar to resistors. Various manufacturers attempted to set up standards by adopting their own particular color codes, until finally some form of standardization was generally adopted and recommended by the Radio and Television Manufacturers' Association.

Some differences will still be encountered in the color coding of certain special type resistors or capacitors, but the color codes presented herein represent those used for the modern types of resistors and capacitors which are likely to be found in computer applications.

Figure A-1 illustrates the generally used type of molded composition resistors, molded capacitors, and the ceramic disc capacitors in use. Figure A-2 shows the color code in use for the molded composition resistors, while Fig. A-3 applies to the molded capacitors and ceramic capacitors shown in Fig. A-1.

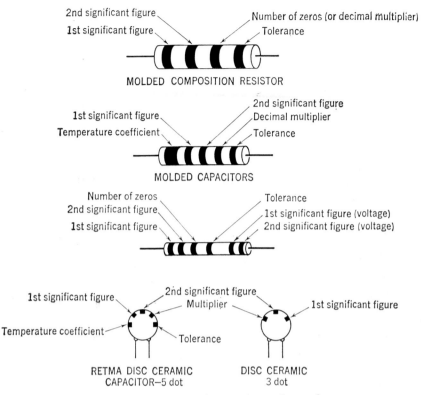

Fig. A-1. Resistor and capacitor color codes.

MOLDED-COMPOSITION FIXED-RESISTOR COLOR CODE

Color	Significant Figure	Multiplying Value
Black	0	1
Brown	1	10
Red	2	100
Orange	3	1,000
Yellow	4	10,000
Green	5	100,000
Blue	6	1,000,000
Violet	7	10,000,000
Gray	8	100,000,000
White	9	1,000,000,000
Gold	± 5% tolerance	0.1
Silver	±10% tolerance	0.01
No Color	±20% tolerance	

Fig. A-2

MOLDED- AND CERAMIC-CAPACITOR COLOR CODE

Color	Significant Figure	No. of Zeros Following Sig. Cap. Fig.	Capacity Tolerance
Black	0		±20%
Brown	1	0	
Red	2	00	
Orange	3	000	±30%
Yellow	4	0000	±40%
Green	5	00000	± 5%
Blue	6	000000	
Violet	7		
Gray	8		
White	9		±10%

Fig. A-3

Two types of molded capacitors are illustrated, the first one having a wide band at the left. This color band indicates the temperature co-efficient of the capacitor. Significant figures and decimal multipliers, as well as tolerance, then follow the sequence for the other type of molded capacitor shown. This second type of molded capacitor has all bands of the same width, with the last two bands utilized for voltage tolerance. This capacitor may also be available without the latter two bands. The sequence of colors in the first molded capacitor is proper when the wide band is at the left. The proper sequence of colors for the second molded capacitor is proper when the two bands which are separated from the other bands are toward the right.

With respect to capacitors, the first two significant figures are the micromicrofarads. The third digit indicates the number of zeros which follow. When voltage bands are present, the voltage rating is identified by a single-digit number for ratings through 900 volts, and a two-digit number for ratings above 900 volts. It is understood that *two zeros* follow the significant figure or figures ascertained by the color code.

Bibliography

Bevitt, William D., *Transistors Handbook*. Englewood Cliffs, N. J.: Prentice-Hall, Inc., 1957. This book covers the characteristics of transistors, with chapters on the junction types, power types, tetrode and pentode types, as well as the photosensitive types. The aspects of practical circuits are stressed throughout the text. Chapter 19 treats transistor relaxation oscillators, including multivibrators, blocking oscillators and flip-flop circuits. Chapter 20 covers computer applications of transistors, with appropriate circuit schematics and discussions of gating, switching, shift registers, adders, and other transistorized computer circuits.

Diebold, John, *Automation*. Princeton, N. J.: D. Van Nostrand Company, Inc., 1952. A book detailing the study of the possibilities, limitations, and economic factors of new electronic machines, their influence on employment and pricing of goods, and the relationship of automation to the standards of living. A nontechnical book without illustrations.

McCracken, D. D., *Digital Computer Programming*. New York: John Wiley & Sons, Inc., 1957. This book provides a general introduction to digital computer programming. It presents fundamental ideas with respect to computer programming, and relates examples and explanations to a mythical computer called TYDAC to illustrate typical programming techniques.

Richards, R. K., *Arithmetic Operations in Digital Computers*. New York: D. Van Nostrand Company, Inc., 1955. Covers design factors involved with respect to the various circuit combinations of computer systems. Boolean algebra is discussed, and there are numerous block diagrams of circuit combinations. Very few schematic representations are included, as emphasis is on the arithmetic aspects of digital computer circuitry.

Wass, C. A. A., *Introduction to Electronic Analogue Computers*. New York: McGraw-Hill Book Company, Inc., 1956. A book covering the fundamental circuits of analog computers. Chapters cover differential
293

analyzers, simple simulators, amplifiers, nonlinear computing elements, and other apparatus.

Wilkes, M. V., *Automatic Digital Computers*. New York: John Wiley & Sons, Inc., 1956. Discusses historical development of digital computers and covers some logical design and programming factors. Also has chapters on storage and switching, and an annotated bibliography.

Index